Fred Johnston

Language classes

on hearing of the death of George MacBeth

Notebooks and coffee, a dry anticipation
It's been twenty-three years since I felt all this
or understood the need for discipline
outside the poetic or the spoken word –

this small learning will travel with us,
tame more passionate tongues in sunnier places
try the old used bluff of pretending
that language is symmetrical and can be measured

your death, meanwhile, had filtered down
a 'phone-line from the BBC, someone listening
for something else heard the report on the news,
you'd spent good years there, so you told me

the time we sank in those monstrous lobby chairs
my note-taking hurried, catching up,
netting in all those dates and names, playing
at journalist again, needing shoes

that sense of style, you said, a poet
should cultivate for himself, not like
the rest, he is something specific –
it was something you carried over from another

time, offering all of it, knowing
the deserving and the sly are indistinguishable
in the soft light of something new, and it takes
too much time and effort to sort them out

break them down to constituent parts –
all morning I've been learning to speak English
again, to pass ragged syntax and eccentric verbs
on down the line to a world unaware of the TLS

to mate subject, verb, object, in some half-
decent comprehensible form, hearing over it all
the metronome of your walking-cane
marking time to an older music.

Tarquintessence

Thomas Allan

Something was bothering me and I didn't know what it was. Oh, all right, I did know what it was. It was those bloody shorts. I mean I was nearly eleven for God's sake. Every boy in my class had long trousers and there was me walking about half-nude. In fact three-quarters nude when you saw just how small they were when I managed to button into them.

I lay in bed and watched them drying on the fireguard. Even here they bothered me. How could I read my book with them eclipsing the fire? I looked up at the lightbulb, half-tempted to get up and switch it on. Even its shadow couldn't make up its mind, splitting into two like the hands on a toy watch that could only give you a shady idea of the time. I blew out a fat sigh. It was hopeless. My mother would hear the switch clicking anyway. Besides, if I fell asleep with the light on and the meter ran dry during the night, then I would be in for it the next day!

Money, money, money. Always money. You would have thought it was important or something. "Money's tight", they kept saying. "Everybody has to cut their cloth."

Well I was cutting mine alright. The cleft of my bum was a well-split peach in those girdling bands of black that passed for school shorts. No wonder the boys smirked and the girls giggled. I could see why for myself – all I had to do was turn tiptoe in the mirror and look down my back and there they were in my reflection: tiny steps of bumps that were my own tailbones, showing up under the cloth, as plain as the spine on a greyhound! And why did my mother have to iron them with diamond precision? My rump, parcelled in pleated drapes, felt as if it was forever on display. It was ridiculous. I couldn't even get my hands in my pockets any more. My front legs looked like two cans wrapped in the one label. And, there, in the middle, my thingymebob was thingymebobbing, forever pulling my zipper down till, eventually, my pants showed through like the white of a split chestnut. I had to 'lock' the zipper with a carefully-hidden safety-pin. The very thought of it had me hiding under the bedclothes.

Oh misery, misery. There was no escape. It even followed me into my dreams. At first everything would be wonderful. I was walking around the playground picking up hundreds of leaves. All kinds of leaves. Red, orange, green – you name it. For some reason these leaves were the running currency of dreamland and I was rummaging up a fortune. I had so much I even threw some in the air. I was rich! "Here everybody – wheeee!"

But then something went wrong with the picture. All the other children were around me in a big circle, all pointing and laughing. I couldn't figure out what was so funny. Then I followed the tips of their pointing fingers. The leaves fell from my arms. I was standing with nothing on but an old vest. When I tried I couldn't even get it to cover my belly-button.

I don't know whether I screamed before or after I awoke. All I knew was that I was sitting bolt-upright in bed, wide-eyed and panting for breath.

The room was dark except for a tiny sunset dying in the black throat of the fire. I held my breath to hear the laughter my penduluming eyes suspected, but there was none. Just the gentle swelling of the linoleum from the draught coming under the door, the tinkling of embers collapsing in the grate; then somebody – or two somebodies – snoring through the wall. The snore was an even see-saw between a whine and a whistle. Definitely two snorers there, cradling each other in their slumber.

I sank into my vest with relief, its straps still standing in loops above my bony shoulders – phew! Then I collapsed back on the pillow and nearly brained myself on the headboard. I had forgotten my mother always nicked the pillow gently from under my head whenever I fell asleep. The bang, I swear, showed me an illuminated crescent of horseshoes in the dark. I could also have sworn I knew what was going to happen next, but it was only a second in eternity, and I lost it straight away.

But my sniffling under the bedclothes was not for the bump on the head. No. It was for me.

It was alright for them in their long trousers, they were fully covered-in. A merry string of cut-out kids straight from a glossy catalogue. I was just a plain, uncrayoned pageboy with a safety-pin to keep his shorts from falling down. I even had a baby shape, like a 'cello sawed in half, curves that were meant for the side profile of a girl. But what was worse was that I knew the other boys were just as 'S'-shaped as me. It was just their clothes that hid it. I could be just as straight up and down as they were if only my mother could have afforded it.

But she couldn't, could she? Still, we had a full week off from school starting from tomorrow. My mother had half-promised that she would get me long trousers for going back. I tried to content myself and go back to sleep. I could always hide for the week.

Then I remembered Sly, and felt even better. Sly was a cur with no fixed abode, half bearded collie and half human: or so it seemed to me, at that age being half a human myself.

It was funny why I should have felt better that night, for it was the very next day that it happened. He had been coming to my back door for weeks now, rustling his furry knoll – which sat on the end of his back for a tail – like a rather damp and depleted straw pom-pom. He always made me laugh, with his beetly eyebrows articulating so comically on his forehead. One brow was black and the other grey. He also had a moustache like an old Hussar's and panted his tongue at you over teeth as sharp as needles. He made me sad too, somehow, to think he had a person inside his nature, a wee vagrant clump of sniffing fur – a brother earthling.

Whenever he wanted a bit of your biscuit, Sly would tilt his head to the side and open a surprisingly pink and silk-lined ear. When he thought a bit was forthcoming he shut his black, lipsticked mouth and waited trance-like, motionless, till the biscuit neared his nose, and then – snap! – before you could change your mind, nearly taking your fingers with it.

He knew that was a bad thing to do, and would try to atone for his greed by bowing his head low and looking up humbly, till you could see the pink rim round the whites of his eyes. If that didn't work he would pretend indifference and sniff mathematics in the dust. Failing that, he might press a passing insect and bring it up for a look on the sole of his pad. Or yawn. With his mouth widening so big it looped his tongue, and shut his eyes until it looked as if he would suck his ears in through the back of his head.

But I never let him suffer too much for his snap-happy hungriness. I would playfully scrub his sconce and he would come out all happy, with his tongue panting with silent laughter. Then his mouth would stiffen to attention again as he watched me eat the last of my biscuit, his hopeful eyebrows tick-tocking on his head in a countdown for more. His gulp was pitiful – a swallow of collected water, almost squeezing down his throat. That always got him the very last bit, even when it was half-posted over my own lips. Fly Sly. He must have belonged to a ventriloquist.

Summer or not, I had to wear my wellingtons (money again). So there I was that morning, pulling them on at the back doorstep, and along came Sly padding around the side of the house.

"Hi, Sly!" I said, fitting the wellies on like a new pair of lower legs. For some reason Sly was much more excited than usual. He could hardly contain himself. Even when I threw him a piece of biscuit he just butted it away, like a seal, using his nose. Then he did a sort of sitting two-step shuffle. I couldn't figure it. Sly not hungry? Maybe he had caught rabies. He kept jumping about and coming back to bow in a low salaam, begging me with a whine so facially suppressed I thought for a second it had come out of his ears. I tried to ignore him and drink my tea, but he suddenly came out with such an unexpected yelp that I found myself sitting with dripping eyebrows. Then he kept running round the side of the house and coming back to see if I was following. Eventually I gave in and did, but I wasn't hurrying just for him.

We lived on the very edge of town that ended in fields just across the road. Sly found a low hole in the hedges and scrambled through into the fields on his belly. I followed.

It was a beautiful summer's day and the sky overhead was a dark ghost above the lighter horizon. The fields and hedgerows sizzled with insect electricity. Sly kept stopping for me to hurry up, but I carried on at a comfortable stroll, chewing on some grass, my thumbs tucked into my tight waistband. I stopped and looked into the cows' drinking bath. Dry and green – empty, with wee earthquakes fracturing the mud at the bottom. The hoof-prints around the sides were a miniature moonscape of dusty craters. I booted two or three of them to powdery explosions, supplying my own sound-effects by growling saliva in the back of my throat. Sly watched it all with his tongue dangling in tolerant exhaustion.

I motioned him to lead on. He led me to the high hedges that surrounded the one house in the whole field. The Rich House, we kids called it, although you could only ever see its roof because of the hedges.

Sly crawled under a hole in the corner. I genuflected under a low branch and found myself in a cool shadowy boundary. Sly summoned up some new-found gaiety and I watched as his furry knoll bounced away into the long grass towards the house. He was obviously used to the place. That's when I heard a voice greeting him in female delight. I bobbed up for a second and that was when I saw her. Down on her knees and hugging Sly's face to her own. A girl, a lady so…

I ran away.

I lingered on the way back across the field to see if Sly would follow. I wondered if that was his real house or what? Maybe he just visited her like me. But most of all, I wondered about the lady. Who was she? Her with that long, cool, brown hair.

I stopped and pondered on a blackened cow-pat, watching the flies, their tiny bodies, compartments of petrol-tank blue, turning about on top of the crust. They didn't move in articulated turns like bees or wasps, but in darts of electrostatic shifts. A shrill movement; not nice. Like they were magnetised toys moved from underneath, shifting in spasms of fixtures. I saw the invisible outlines of their fixed wings catching glints of white plastic light, evil capes of transparencies. There were so many of them they made me scratch.

But who was the lady so… so good? I looked back at the house. I knew I would go back tomorrow. And of course I did. Every day for that week. And she was always there. My lady mine.

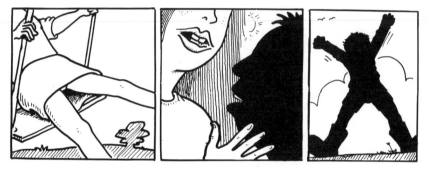

I suppose she was a lady then, although she could have been no more than sixteen, but that was the oldest you got to then, before diminishing into a shrinking old age. Sixteen was the height and square of your ultra-extremities. Then you got married and shrunk into wee mums and dads.

I sometimes went more than once in the same day to see her, watching from the safety of the trees. A rich girl, all on her own; all my own.

She seemed fond of her own company. Liked it. Shared it with the petals of a flower she liked to pluck, split it with a blade of grass to explore some theory. When she lay on her belly, she would dangle her legs, crossed at the angles, with her toes pointing at the sky, humming to herself and staring through her long hair as she toyed with some daisy buttoned fast to the green earth. She seemed a sort of indolent American rich-kid, fantasising. I don't know why American: she just looked… American. Sort of acting out a part in some film. I used to think she might be a mad girl, locked away here, out of sight, lost in her strange song of glee.

Sometimes she sat on a big swing under a tree, dallying her toes and studying them like some women study their manicured fingers. Her head tilted to each shoulder, then she would giggle as if she knew something really naughty about them, something I burned to know too.

Other times she would stroll quite near, and I would sink so low that I could smell worms but still watch her as she went by above me with that slow, leg-at-a-time movement, her shoulders swinging with the idleness of the gait and her head to the side in that half-mad lullaby.

Sometimes I suspected that she knew I was there, or at least hoped I was; hoped *somebody* was. If she didn't, then it was an act. A strange act of playing at being afraid. Her fingers spread backwards on her cheeks as she peered in terror into the bushes, like the screaming lady in *King Kong*. Only my lady never let the scream out, but stood there aghast at something I couldn't see in the trees behind me. A something that often worried me too, but which never came to get her – thank God!

But it was on the swing that I liked her best. She was good on that. Lying straight back as she swung with her hair trailing in the grass, her eyes closed, her body straight, she would swing slowly to the see-saw snoring of the creaking branch. Sometimes the wind billowed her dress and I could see her resplendent pink pants. I gaped intently, engulfed in a rising tendency to choke. I couldn't understand the feeling, all I knew was that I liked it, liked that awful longing for God-knew-what. I even went hard in embarrassment for her not knowing that I was looking up her dress. It was funny how girls' pants always embarrassed me the hardest 'there'. I was sure I could feel the safety-pin bending, but I couldn't turn away. Couldn't if I had wanted to. I didn't want to.

I just zeroed in on her swinging, enticing body. Me, a leopard, low-slung in the long grass, my shoulderblades up and rubbing in the middle of my nape, my mind burning, burning, burning. The pain in my crotch aching with every pulse, going mad with an unknown guiltiness, turning animal, stalking, lurking…preying.

And always, too soon, it was over. She would struggle up from her dizzying swing and lean her pink exhausted face against the rope. Her eyes still closed, panting for breath, as if she too… as if she too… as if she too…what?

I angrily didn't know. Angrily didn't. Very, very angrily.

Then she would slip wearily off the swing, only letting go of the rope at the break of her outstretched departure, a soft, dull, soundless twang. Then she was going, dusting the rope-dust off her dress; indifferent to me, her audience of one, as she went into the house to recover from her own unknown sickening, to rehearse for her next audition.

And out I go too. Out through the high, high hedges. A malcontent.

Across the fields towards home, the tartan head of the monarch thistle comes up before me. A small Christmas tree all to itself, starchy-leafed with a furzy purple plume, its pointed thorns joining fingers as a cue ready for a highland fling. A fascist crest to its own proud self.

I pick up a stick and behead her, her broken neck dangling by the one strand of fibre. "Mary, Queen of Scots."

One day she found me. Saw me up among the branches of a tree. She walked over slowly and curiously, her eyes, lit by the sun, brown and blood-rich. They looked on me intensely, two newly-minted coins of light. She twined the tresses of her hair slowly around her long, bamboo-cane fingers. She stopped below and looked up – and smiled!

"Come down, boy", she said in a soft command, like an imperious Alice from Wonderland. I slid down, a frightened native, my shirt unbuttoning in my hesitant slithering, my shorts painted green by the bark, my thighs rubbed to a carbolic pink. Her eyes appraised me as she sucked on an end of her hair. My heart was thumping in my ears – I was sure they were swelling at every beat. I know I was breathing hard, an animal at bay... caught. No longer mythical, even to myself, but a creature of intensity. She took her fascinated eyes off me for a second and cast a glance round at the big house. Then, sure that nobody had seen us, she stole me by the hand to a shady corner and there she bent and kissed me. A ripple of warmth swam slowly from her lips to mine. She stood up straight and cornered a tress of hair over the beautiful shell of her ear just to see, and be seen, better. Her face questioned mine with her soul in her eyes.

It was then that I ran away. In spite of her plea to wait, I ran hard out across the field, my shirt billowing, my wellingtons ricochetting with splitting grass, their rims flip-flopping around my pumping knees.

I reached the cows' bath, jumped up and stood openly astride it, my arms out in a great big 'V'. I jumped off with my spearless fists clenched in triumph. "Yes!"

Thomas Allen

AN AULD SANG DIRLS AGAIN!

the CEILIDH HOUSE

The **H**igh **S**treet wis yince a hub o music, poetry an' talk.
The **C**eilidh **H**ouse pits back that tradeetioun.
Folk nichts — poetry nichts — an aye-bidan come-aa-ye

ilka nicht o the week a new stramash!

Cleik yer pals in fur a pint or a dram. Ye'll hae a waarm walcome.

Eldritch neuks and crannies fur smaa foregaitherings
Cellar haa fur middlin-scale occasiouns

The Ceilidh House, 9 Hunter Square, Edinburgh EH1 1QW
Heid Wanger: Cy Laurie
Tel 031-220 1550

Linda McCann

The Recidivist

He wanted locking up.
We even suspected
he set off alarms and waited,
resisted arrest to be arrested.
Once he stole a can of lager in Tesco's,
cracking it open
while edging sideways
through the ten items or less.
Then today I heard he'd checked out
with the courage of his conviction,
died happy on the threshold
of a six-month stretch.
Until the moment he was lifted
people had looked the other way
in a Saturday night pub
as he made for the jaws
of the outside world,
a full charity bottle
clasped in his arms like a baby.

Mooning

The moon is half-closed
in a spreading bruise
a real shiner.
Old nightwatchman
turning up for work
hungover on moonshine.

Nature's above art

In his offhand way, he handed me a rose –
everlasting – too realistic to be real.
I thumbed the wax green of the stem,
fingered the grain of a petal's weave –
but as though it became a serpent
and lashed from my hand, I let go
and watched it grow more perfect
with each worm hole and brown edge
then, as though retractable,
scores of tiny thorns began to bristle.

Metaphors

the best words come
dream drifting
but try to net them, light and pen
and they surge away
on the shift in consciousness.
A tape recorder wouldn't do.
Thought recorder maybe,
machine of the mind –
but what background noise might
twist the undercurrent?

Panning for poems
I pore through old notebooks
watching for a glint,
trail slow silver
to contact lost emotions,
wait and measure old meaning
out of time,
place and focus,
try not to try for
that accidental alchemy.

I collect my thoughts on paper,
miser pennies in a jar
one day to add up
to notes of value.
Then sometimes late at night
I grub for words
that race across the page,
and corner demons loiter,
ex-double-glazing salesmen
with soul-selling folders.

The sweet smell of calor gas
shiver. Squeeze the foot
into the glass slipper.
Gather the drops of blood.

Swings and Roundabouts

I wrote my first poem aged five –
shouted it – from a high swing:
The sun the sun is in the sky,
Shining down on you and I.
What? said my big brother's wife
then she laughed and told me it was wrong.
She's a teacher now.

Then when I was nine Miss Finlay
opened my desk that wouldn't close
and shredded its surplus contents
with her bare fingertips,
an example for my class.

I was as hard as the green metal bin
the paper snowflakes melted into,
vain stories torn to the letter,
my children trapped on a roundabout,
buried alive in their little plots.

At home, primary verses
glanced on coffee tables,
with the so-what stamp of tea-rings,
a scale of one to ten.

Then when I was seventeen
my mother burned love letters
from The Animal, and
guilty by association,
my other fireproof contents,
clang of tin light
on my bedroom floor.

And still I pour myself black and blue –
strange that rejected people
choose rejection slips as a way of life.

And now my lover's sister tells me
that she used to write poems –
but she grew out of it.
As if she'd caught me out
playing on the swings.

Catriona Malan

Love affair with mussels

They clacked, our kidnapped mussels
Barbered, bowl-bathed in strange water,
Blue skins scrubbed
Clean of the sea's licking,
As we tipped them into the pot
And watched them jostle in the bubbles.

On our bed the kicked sheet
Was a cloth tide ebbing
While I clung to you
As our waves roughened,
As breathless we reached the shore,
Your skin salty against my lips
And beyond the blind
The traffic's surf roaring.

We dashed the mussels'
Gaping throats with wine,
Doused them with parsley,
Which caught like cheerless
Confetti on their saffron flesh
And stole from our mouths
The taste of each other.

Astrality

He dreams of me:

I dare not sleep for fear
That, from deep furls of dreams,
His want will steal me down,
Distant where he lies
Fingering his flesh
As a Greek his worry-beads.

So in the drifted dark
My closed lips curse him
In his trembled certainty
That it was I trespassed,
And roused him from
Innocent sleep.

Prisoner of conscience

Hold tight – tighter than the rules
That lock your freedom.

How small the floor that bears,
Like bruises, the shadow of bars.

How small the window-square that lets
The sky turn yet confiscates the stars.

Unlipped in your silent mouth
Lie countless words

Whose whisper could overwhelm
The howling.

Beyond the walls' album of scratches
Mouths you cannot imagine have cried your name;

Those cries, were each a raindrop,
Could shout down a deluge.

Make from your conviction an ark.
Embark your words and sail your ocean,

And hold tight – till the dove
Finds the mountain-top.

Photograph of a skater

When I look at this moment –
Its wrought-iron trees,
Scars whitening the pond's skin
And the hills beyond sulking
Under their cold fleece –

I can hear
Your blades' scrape
And the whispered protest
Of reeds nipped by ice;
How the crows on their ragged way
Called hollow in the blanched sky
And my name rang
Cloudy from your throat;

Reminding me that,
As the sun smouldered down
Your red hat still burned
In frosty circuits
Until you slid over to test
Cold lips on the warmth of my mouth
And we stayed till the plough
Began to cut its glittering fields;

So the figure-eight you scratched,
Turning with winged arms
On the greying ice,
Is frozen
Here, in this moment.

The Tool Chest

Iain Crichton Smith

When Donald came from the island to visit us, he was at first very depressed, as he had had a hard lonely winter. We used to hear him praying in the middle of the night, groaning and sighing and saying, "God have pity on me." He would sit for hours without speaking, or go to his room and read the bible. We found his silences oppressive. We tried to take him out on visits: at first he would say he was coming with us and then he would change his mind at the last minute.

He wore a black hat and a big black jacket, though the weather was sultry and close. His face was fixed and pale and strained, and he would often press his hand to his eyes as if he were suffering from a headache. His arm too was swollen with some mysterious ailment.

One morning he decided to go down to the shed which we have in the field below the house. There are actually two sheds, one a proper bought shed which was taken home from a firm and assembled, and a large black byre which has almost been flattened by the wind, the door hanging open. The windows of both buildings have been smashed by young local boys who cross the field in the evening to play football in a neighbouring park. He was suddenly quite happy searching in the shed, for it was full of boxes containing tools of all kinds.

He said, "You don't have a tool chest in the house, I've noticed. How don't you have one: Every house should have a tool chest." And he looked at me accusingly. Of course I never used tools much myself, preferring to pay tradesmen for any jobs that had to be done. In any case I was what they call handless. He muttered again to himself, as if he couldn't imagine how anyone could exist without having a tool chest.

Sometimes when I saw him walking about near the house, I thought he was going to fall down. He was of course eighty-five years old, and ever since the death of his wife he hadn't been well, catching colds every winter, as his house which stood on a headland near the sea was draughty and damp. Often he would say, "The body is weak, but the mind is still clear."

So he decided that he would build us a tool chest. He found some old pieces of wood, a hammer, a rusty-toothed saw, and a chisel, and he carried them up through the long wet grass of the field, past the little snarling dogs which belonged to our neighbour and which barked at him incessantly. Most of the time his chest was sizzling as if he had asthma.

He took his booty down to the back of the house and began to build the tool chest. Suddenly his life appeared to take on point and meaning, though he was still puffing and panting, and it occurred to me that he felt that he ought to be paying us for his holiday and that this was his method of doing so.

Anyway, the tool chest became the centre of the day for us. I had to discontinue my own work and help him with the sawing while he directed operations.

"Not like that", he would say to me irritably. "You have to cut with a steady movement."

The work was hard and I found the sawing difficult, especially as the saw was quite old and rusty. Meanwhile Donald held down the plank of wood while I sawed. He was of course often complaining that the tools were inadequate. "I need a spirit level," he would say, "and you don't have a plane either."

The sawing took rather a long time, as we were often interrupted by showers of rain. We were in fact worried that he would catch a cold, and would bring him in at the first drops. If the rain lasted a long time he would continue with a book about Martin Luther which he was reading. At times his lips were blue and we thought he was going to have a heart attack, and we would tell him that he should stop work for the day. But he was very stubborn and he would answer, "I don't like to leave a job unfinished. It preys on my mind." But I would say to him, "You have another fortnight of your holiday left", and he would reply sharply, "You never know the day or the hour."

Actually, I was at first irritated that I couldn't carry on with my own writing, but he didn't think that my work was of any importance. In his eyes the tool chest was a much superior project. When I stayed in my work room he would come looking for a pencil, and so I had to go out to the tool chest again. I spent hours screwing nails into wood for him. He was a perfectionist: often he had to remove a piece of wood because it wasn't exactly in the right place: and all the time his chest was puffing like an engine and his face was pale and gaunt.

If we had bought a tool chest we wouldn't have had all this hassle, I told my wife. We could even have had bright new wood, instead of these warped planks. For the wood he was using was of inferior quality, and as he didn't have proper tools he had to be content with approximate measurements, which enraged him. In fact the tool chest was rather ramshackle, as it consisted of different kinds of wood, some of which had been painted and some not. The top was an old sheet of iron which he hammered flat. All in all it wasn't a beautiful artefact, though as good as his materials would permit.

However, he was no longer depressed, and indeed in the evening he would talk about the day's work and about the work which, if God permitted, might be done on the following day. He was very knacky and skilful with his hands, there was no doubt about that. But if we praised the tool chest he would say, "No, it's a poor thing. I'm not happy with it, but what can you do if you don't have the tools. If it had been twenty years ago..." And he would sigh heavily.

Tools were real, I thought, wood was real, and while all the real things existed I was working on my stories in my quiet room. At the side of the fence where we worked at the back of the house, the ferns climbed, a tall dense green jungle. He was trying to make a sliding panel from a piece of wood that had been painted green.

So it had been with early man when he discovered tools. He had differentiated himself from the insatiable greenery round him, he had separated himself from the grass, he had stood isolated and upright in the world. By the sweat of his brow he had earned his bread.

He adopted a teasing attitude to me. He would call me Charlie. "Oh, Charlie did a good job today with the screwdriver", he would say to my wife. "He'll make an apprentice yet." And he would laugh, for he knew that I wasn't an adept worker with tools.

The tool chest had become the centre of our lives; it was necessary that he finish it before he returned to his draughty room and the attention of caring neighbours on the island.

"There is an old woman beside me," he told us, "and she won't have a home help. She plants the potatoes every year, and she's eighty-eight. But there's another one who reads romances all the time and smokes like a chimney."

Though his health seemed to be improving during the day, at night I could hear him coughing and spluttering and praying very loudly. It sounded strange to hear that intense voice calling on God at four in the morning.

He will die here, we worried, making this tool chest, and we felt guilty about it. What does he feel that he owes us? But then I thought, if he does die it would be better for him to do so while working. At first certainly I had tried to keep him in the house, but later as time passed, I saw that the freedom of building the tool chest was necessary to him. After all, didn't I have the urge of creativity myself, though in my case it was the compulsion to create stories, and in his to work with tools.

Sometimes he would stay out when it was raining, in spite of our protests. "No, it's only a few drops", he would say, and put on his black hat so that against the background of ferns and leaves he looked like a minister in an orchard.

I disregarded my writing and stayed out with him. I watched him and learned a lot. For instance, before putting a screw in the wood he would hammer a nail in first to make a hole. Actually he didn't have the strength to put the screw in himself and relied on me to do that.

In the evenings, as time went on, he would relax and talk to us. He would say, "The worst job I have at home is the dishes.

"The morning I left to come down here, I thought I would not be able to rise from my bed. I managed it however, and a man on the boat took my case up the gangway for me. But I've got good neighbours, I really have. On my right there's a young couple who are very kind to me, and then in front of me there's an older couple, and they paid my electricity bill for me when I was out here on holiday last time. I leave them the key, you see. And then further up the street there's a retired nurse who takes me to church every Sunday in her car.

"The only problem I have is that I don't want to eat anything I cook myself. All last winter I could only eat jellies because my stomach was bad.

"But there's one thing sure, this holiday has done me the world of good. I feel better in every way, and Donalda's cooking is first rate."

One day I went to the back of the house to call him in for his dinner. He was bending over the tool chest, which was almost finished. He was puffing and panting and taking deep breaths.

I saw the open shelves of the box and it seemed to me for a moment as if it was the box he would shortly inhabit. I imagined his face rigid and stern as he lay in that box, his nose pointing towards the saw-toothed mountains of the west.

Suddenly he heard my footsteps and straightened up. He made a conscious effort to keep from coughing. He took the hammer again in his hand.

And just as suddenly the box seemed to put on a green foliage. Flowers both red and white rose from it. And he stood in the middle of the foliage, old and upright, the hammer blunt and solid in his hand, though it looked rusty enough in the bright sparkling and eternally young light.

Murdo at the BBC

Iain Crichton Smith

When Murdo was invited to a Glasgow studio at the BBC to talk about his new book *The Thoughts of Murdo*, he spoke for a while about literary matters such as his train journey, what he had for breakfast, and his expenses.

That done he launched into praising his book which he said was modelled on *The Thoughts of Chairman Mao*, Mao being, he understood, the Chinese equivalent of Murdo.

He suggested very strongly that if the listener was of the ilk which hadn't smiled for a long time e.g. a Celtic supporter, he should buy the book and, addressing his listeners directly, he continued, you will find here anarchic ideas, revolutionary concepts, animadversions on the laughable nature of reality in which we are all enmired. If, he went on, you are moved to laughter by the signing of the Magna Carta or the Monroe Doctrine, or the Scottish International Football Team, you will find here much to amuse: if you think that MacGonagall was a great creative genius; if you enjoy the catastrophes that happen to other people, then you will enjoy this book. If you like similes such as, ·e.g., as hectic as a cucumber, as foreign as an eel, or as brave as a traffic warden, you will find such plays on words here. Indeed the pun is part of its essence such that you may hear a pun drop or indeed a pan drop. Other topics adumbrated are *Neighbours* and *Take the High Road*.

Moreover, he continued, humour breaks down all boundaries except those between Lewis and Harris. It raises a smile in toilets and in supermarkets, it joins us all together by elasticated bands, it breaks down dogmas (such as e.g. love me, love my dogma), it recognises the futility

of all effort, reconstitutes well-known poems into new language such as 'When I consider what my wife has spent', by Milton, it creates new denouements for books, and so on. All these you will find in this valuable though not priceless volume.

It has been said of me that I am the greatest humorist since Ecclesiastes or Job. While not disputing that for a moment, let me add that in buying this book you will be joining a certain class of people as ignorant as yourselves, uninterested in such serious topics as litter, and able to lie in bed for a long period of time without moving. Your vacant gaze will be fully reflected in this book, as also your anthropoid opinions. Verbs, adverbs and nouns will turn somersaults, and you will see the triviality of all that passes for power and progress e.g. Visa Cards, the Westminster Confession etc.

If you are of that ilk which yearns for meaninglessness, I am your instant guru. I sign no agreements without laughter, I am an enemy of the working breakfast. A book such as mine will give you arguments for maintaining a prudent lethargy, and for avoiding tax; it will sustain you in your night of deepest laziness; and will remind you of famous figures which include Mephistopheles and Mrs. Robb, 3 Kafka Rd., East Kilbride.

If you wish for history, you will not find it here, you will not be burdened by anthropology, genealogies or any formal logic. The Chaos

Theory will not be examined even with a broad brush, nor will there be much reference to thermodynamics. Dante however gets a brief mention. Cultural influences on the whole will be avoided and there are no quotations from St. John of the Cross. Some reference however is made to herring and to those golden days when you could buy a tenement for sixpence. Clichés as far as they are understood will not be used and neither will metonymy, synecdoche, personification etc. Wittgenstein along with Partick Thistle will be relegated, and so will remarks of football managers such that 'If you do not score goals you will never win a match.'

If you are looking for passion you will have to look elsewhere. Enthusiasm is avoided as is any form of élan or hope. Optimism is evaded and no one learns by experience. It has taken the writer many years to arrive at this position, having endured friendly fire etc. and he is now as happy as a red herring in May.

He no longer believes that the British working man will ever come to repair any form of machinery. He eschews the illusion of efficiency. He believes that the class system will remain unchanged, and that television will not be better than it is today. British Rail will fail and MacBraynes will be as grass. Asses will be coveted and adultery will rear its ugly head. The Royal Family will perish in the Bog of the Tabloid, and the Queen will reign forever, though otherwise the weather will not be too bad. Middle-of-the-road politics will be run over by speedsters, and sanity will no longer be accepted as an alibi.

In conclusion buy this book, as it will not be published again in a hurry, unless there is a great demand for animadversions on hopelessness.

And finally God bless you all, though the probability is that he will not.

Iain Crichton Smith in conversation

Bill Duncan

Bill Duncan: *How do you feel about being the second Scottish poet after Norman MacCaig to be made the subject of study in this way?*

Iain Crichton Smith: I suppose it's quite flattering, really. Apart from that, it probably means that the pupil will never read me again after the exam! I think some of the themes are quite difficult, and may not be immediately interesting, particularly the religious one. It may not be the kind of thing that young people look for in poetry nowadays.

I do feel, though, that challenging poems are good for people. When I was a teacher myself I didn't like to take slight poems about which I could find very little to say. I think with these poems in general there's plenty for pupils to analyse. Some of the poems are very accessible: 'Gaelic Songs' for instance, and 'Old Woman'.

Do you feel there is some prior knowledge that a 16/17-year-old would need in order to come to some understanding of your poetry?

I suppose some of the poems depend on a certain autobiographical element. One should know something about Lewis and the kind of religion that is the background there. One should know something about Lewis being an island from which there has been a lot of emigration. The background isn't too difficult. A little reading would help.

Which writers have influenced your own development as a writer?

When I was about eleven and first started writing, I used to like Keats, Scott, Shelley, Kipling: poets that had a sonorous quality about their work, because at that age I didn't like reading poetry silently. For some reason I had to read poetry aloud. Many years afterwards when I was in university I remember going around Old Aberdeen which was very granite and reciting aloud lines from *Othello* which seemed to me very suitable to Aberdeen because of the mineral imagery: "Put up your bright swords or the dew will rust them." I liked those kinds of things, but as I went through university I read Eliot who had an influence on me, and Auden who had an immediate influence. Later, the American poet Robert Lowell was another important influence.

How do you see the current literary scene in Scotland?

I think the present period will be looked back on as one of the great ages of Scottish literature. I particularly like Stewart Conn's work, because of the sense of vulnerability which I find in it and which is so prominent in my own work. There are a number of younger writers as well, some of them in Gaelic. I like James Kelman and Allan Massie, though the two are completely different. Kelman is in a sense more local, while Massie is writing about Europe and has a more European consciousness. I liked the recent *Swing Hammer, Swing!* by Jeff Torrington and I think that Alasdair Gray's *Poor Things* was excellent, very finely written and beautifully presented. There are more and more fine Scottish writers emerging all the time. In some ways I think Scottish prose is stronger than English because someone like Kelman is dealing with experiences that English writers just don't seem to have coped with: they seem to be tremendously middle-class. They don't confront the poverty of the people and they haven't tried to find a voice for it, and I think Kelman has.

What memories do you have of your time as a teacher?

When I was doing sixth year studies at Oban High School I was doing Freud and Marx and Einstein and introducing ideas of the twentieth century as well as talking about literature. I found that extremely interesting, in fact it was the thing I liked best of all. I used to do psychology with them and in fact some pupils actually took up psychology rather than English eventually.

I taught Sixth Year Studies creative writing. That was one of the papers they could choose and a lot of them did. I found there was quite a big difference between the qualities of the people, for instance, taking Higher English and getting good grades there, and the ones who got good grades for Sixth Year Studies. There was one girl who got a 'C' for English and an 'A' in Sixth Year Studies, mainly because she had this talent for poetry that had never been tested before.

I think Sixth Year Studies and the study and writing of poetry was a way of opening students' minds out. I used all sorts of methods in creative writing. Typically I would formulate something I would like them to do, for instance write a poem about the *Titanic*. I would discuss what happened, play them the hymn 'Nearer my God to thee'; I would then ask them about the kinds of thing that might be found in the water, as it's obviously a very rich upper-class ship. I'd be getting them to work through imagery all the time. Having gathered these images together they could start writing. I would maybe use a poem like Thomas Hardy's 'The *Titanic*' to show them what had already been done, or, if they wanted further things I would suggest that the *Titanic* was a symbol for the first world war, that the sinking of the *Titanic* was the sinking of the upper classes. All these things had to be fed in and then they could select something out of that.

Do you have any conception of an audience when you write poetry?

No. I know that certain people who write blockbuster novels have, and they write towards a market. What I'm trying to do when I write a poem, which may come upon me quite unexpectedly, is almost to put down what an inner voice is telling me to put down. The poem is therefore unpredictable and not made in that very fixed way.

Can I ask you about the creative process generally. How do you write a poem? Do you start off with a group of words, or a message to put across? What is the starting point?

It's very hard to describe. For the moment I'll characterise this as far as a poem is concerned. The best poems, to me, do not arise by an act of will. They arise, you might almost say, randomly. Obviously, they're not random, but at the same time you cannot deliberately set out and create a poem. It's as if some kind of internal music starts and this begins to be associated with words, and sometimes the music is more important than the words. I'll give you this example. The other day my wife was paying someone. She had her purse with her and she took this money out and instantaneously there came into my mind something my mother used to do. Of course, we were very poor when I was growing up. My mother would take out her purse and count the money, because she didn't have very much. Then I started writing about seven sections of a poem, maybe about six lines each, quite spontaneously and without effort. It was a gift. Some poems are gifts. My long poem 'Deer on the High Hills' arose when I was coming home from Glasgow and I saw those deer on the road on a frosty night. Somehow or other an image came into my head of dancers on a ballroom floor and this set it all off. A lot of that poem I don't really understand myself because it operates purely by images. The best poems always seem to come in that 'given' way. You can work on them after they've been given, and you can change within the terms of the poem what you've already done, but there must be an initial part that's given.

What degree of reworking is typically involved in your poetry?

I do more now, I think, mainly because I have more time than I had when I was teaching. But sometimes I find the best poems very hard to redraft, because I feel instinctively that if I try to make them more accessible and more logical they will lose something. An instance of this is a poem written by Auden many years ago. It had a line "we must love one another or die". Years afterwards, he was collecting his poems and going over them and thought "we die anyway, so this doesn't make sense." He then changed it to "we must love one another *and* die" but then it becomes a truism. In contrast, the first, unworked line was echoing with all kinds of mysterious phrases. When he tried to make it more logical it lost its resonance. I think it's sometimes best that there are certain areas of a poem which you feel instinctively should not be touched, even though maybe you don't even fully understand it yourself.

What themes link the twelve selected poems?

I think a Highland ambience is present in many of them, certainly 'The Iolaire', 'The Exiles', 'At the Highland Games' and 'Gaelic Songs'. One of the themes is the Highland one of passionate exile and its kind of tragedy. 'At the Highland Games' is more acerbic. There are a number of poems about women: 'Old Woman', 'You'll take a bath', 'You lived in Glasgow', and 'Two Girls Singing', and I think that's another theme.

Some of the poems have an elusive, unresolved quality which is very characteristic of your work. Poems like 'At the Sale', 'At the Firth of Lorne', 'Hallowe'en, 'The Exiles' and 'Two Girls Singing'. Is this because you don't always have conscious control over your poems when you write, and do you see this openness as a kind of strength?

One of the things I'm very strongly against, partly because of my upbringing, is dogma. Dogma teaches people to give superficial answers to very profound questions. I feel that a lot of my poetry is questioning, rather than providing answers. It may provide an emotional answer rather than an intellectual answer. Many of my poems are questions about things that happen. 'The Iolaire' in particular was a tremendously difficult one to write because the situation it was based on was so extraordinary. That hundreds of men returning from four years at war should be drowned on the shores of their own island was such a difficult event. It could hardly be possible to provide a rational answer to that kind of problem. All one can do is to open out the problem in all its manifestations and let the reader think about the answer.

I think what you're saying has some important implications for the classroom because so many of us, teachers and pupils alike, are obsessed with 'the answer'. Sometimes the lack of a clear-cut answer can unsettle people and I feel that many of your poems don't function this way at all.

No, they don't function in this way and sometimes I find myself unable to provide an intellectual answer, though the emotional weight of a poem may itself resolve something for the reader.

There is a critical theory, structuralism and post-structuralism, where people say that the poem is just a text. Any reader brings their own life experience to a text and the author is not privileged in explaining the text. That is to say, the author's explanation of the text is no more valid than the explanations of any other person. In other words, you can't say "I'll give you 9/10 for your interpretation. I've got my interpretation and the closer you get to this, the better your chance of 10/10." This is not what the theory says: the theory is saying that different people bring different life experiences to the same text, so the analysis and feeling for that text will vary from person to person.

One of the key elements in *Consider the Lilies* was the way in which the old woman went to see the minister. Of course, the minister was entrenched on the other side and she couldn't understand this and why the minister hadn't helped her. As she was coming home she was crossing this rickety little bridge and she fell into the water. My reason for doing this was because I wanted her to be helped by an atheist called Donald McLeod. She wouldn't normally go to speak to him so I had to find some way to get her to his house. What happened was that his two sons were playing near the water. They ran home and told their father and she was taken to his house. To me, it was a question of solving a mechanical problem in the novel. Someone asked me about the significance of this episode, putting forward the idea that the old woman before she fell in the water was Old Testament and when she came out she was New Testament with the water as a form as baptism. It can be read like that, though I never consciously thought of doing it that way. As long as the criticisms are relevant and internally self-consistent, that's fair enough.

What are the starting points for, say, a novel or a short story?

I can give you an instance of how I wrote a short story. In the school I attended, the Nicolson Institute in Stornoway, there was a man, a Maths teacher, and a woman in the Science Department, and they had been engaged for about twenty-five years. All the pupils knew about this and everyone talked about it. Many years later I saw in *The Stornoway Gazette* that the man had died in an old folk's home, never having married. I remembered that when I was a pupil he had sent me into Stornoway for Beecham's Powders for his stomach, as he used to get into terrible rages when he was teaching. So, of course, I brought this up and told everybody he sent me for Beecham's Powders which I thought was very comic.

Now when he died I had this impulse to write a story about him. I used some of the material from what actually happened, but changed it slightly. In the story I still went out for the Beecham's Powders, but when I came back I went to his room and he wasn't there, so I walked along this long stone corridor to the staffroom and I saw two people at the far end of the corridor. As I was walking along, a ring rolled along beside my feet. What happened was the two of them had finally quarrelled and she had thrown the ring. The whole point of the story was, being eleven years old, I didn't understand what was happening. Now the ring wasn't in the original events but I needed something in order to make it a story rather than an anecdote. Sometimes you can use things like this, that have happened to you in your life, and transform them.

Is it fair to see your novel Consider the Lilies *as a central work? I'm thinking of its stylistic accessibility for a start. Also for the way it seems to address key aspects of your work – The Old Woman, Religion, Gaelic and English culture, the village and the city, exile and emigration.*

Yes, I think I would say that *Consider the Lilies* is a key work because it's got the theme of the Old Woman in it. This is a theme that interests me quite a lot – in fact it obsessed me. Also, another theme which is central to my work is my hostility to all forms of ideologies like The Church, but generally speaking any form of ideology which tries to make people conform. The whole idea of the novel was to take a woman who was carapaced in this religious ideology and break it like you would break an egg and then she would come out of it at the end of the book totally vulnerable but more human. She emerges as a totally different person, human and willing to discuss her weaknesses. Vulnerability in my work is also a key element, as well as this hostility to protective ideologies.

If we can move on to some specific poems, 'The Exiles' is fourteen lines long, with an apparent octet and sestet structure. Was it originally a sonnet, with a rhyme scheme lost in your own translation from the Gaelic?

No. It was originally written in Gaelic and possibly some of the rhymes have been lost, but that's always the case when you translate from one language to another. You lose some of the music, though you can retain the meaning. But the music is as important in poetry as the meaning.

'Hallowe'en' seems to be based on a specific incident but there's a definite sense of mystery and strangeness in that poem.

Myself and my wife were in a particular house one night at Hallowe'en and these children came in. Normally when you ask children to sing, or tell a joke, or a story, they will. These particular children, though, were deeply hidden by their masks and didn't say anything! They just went back out into the night. It was like an apparition.

Two of the listed poems, 'You lived in Glasgow' and 'You'll take a bath' appear to deal with reactions to events in your mother's life. Could you say a little about where your mother lived at various points in her life?

My mother lived in Glasgow for quite a while, married there and went up to Lewis. My father died and later, about 1950, she went back to the mainland and stayed in Dumbarton. So the poems refer to two totally separate periods. 'You lived in Glasgow' refers to a period when she would have been young, back in the 1920s, while 'You'll take a bath' would refer to Dumbarton. By this time I was teaching in Oban and coming down at weekends to visit her.

Focussing on specific poems on Lewis and Glasgow, island and city, I was interested in the rather bleak portrayal of Glasgow that emerges. Is that simply a reflection of your circumstances at the time, or is it related to a more deep-seated feeling about Glasgow, or cities in general?

That's an interesting question, as I was actually born in Glasgow and came to Lewis when I was about one year old, and all my University years were spent in Aberdeen. It seemed to me in some ways a more accessible city than Glasgow. For many years I thought of Glasgow as a very raw city. When I first went there I found it quite frightening, and it was only a few years ago when I was visiting Professor at Strathclyde University that I got to know Glasgow better and I became quite familiar with it. Remember, coming from Lewis I had never seen a train until I was seventeen! When I came to Glasgow I found it much bigger than Aberdeen and in some ways much bleaker. I found it uglier and more industrial.

Was it something to do with the lack of a sense of community you felt there, as this is something that comes through strongly in your Lewis work?

Yes, that's probably got a lot to do with it. Funnily enough, Aberdeen seemed more like an overgrown town than a city, so one couldn't get lost in it in the way one could easily get lost in Glasgow. I've grown to like Glasgow much, much more as I've become more familiar with it.

Some of the memorable figures in your work are females, in particular the Old Woman and the Young Girl. Could you shed some light on the prominence of these opposites?

I suppose a lot of the old women were portraits of my mother. I was fascinated by the kind of person my mother was: very religious and, like many of these women of the time, full of certainty. Not cultured, in any real sense, but very strong and not the type of person who would ever say they were sorry because they nearly always believed they were right. I always felt, being changeable and vulnerable in my ideas (like most people in the twentieth century) that this kind of thing both attracted and repelled me. It attracted me because it would be nice to have such certainty, but it also repelled me: there was something about it that I didn't like. The young girl's prevalence is simply based on the idea of youth and freshness, not on a particular girl.

With regard to 'Old Woman (and she, being old)', it seems to me that this poem is characteristic of much of your early work, in this case the contrast between the predicament of the old man and woman in the early parts and the very different images of power and freedom in the later parts. These kinds of oppositions seem crucial in the earlier poems.

Yes, and I'll answer this by referring to another early poem 'Old Woman (your thorned back)'. The old woman in that poem was one of the Calvinist old women that I knew on Lewis. She seems to me to be un-free in her nature and to impose this on others; the idea of the deer and the daffodils suggests the opposite: freedom and beauty. Also in 'The Iolaire' there is the figure of the Elder looking at the wreck and this is contrasted with the image of the sea, which one thinks of as being fluid, whereas the figure of the Elder one thinks of as being static. In 'At the Highland Games' an old conception of what the Highlands were like and the values they once had is contrasted with, to my mind, the superficial glitter of these lairds. Yes, there are a lot of opposites here: it's something I often do. Another thing I've noticed is that many of the poems on the list are strongly metrical in form, which again is often characteristic of my work.

I notice a great deal of daffodil imagery, particularly the poems dealing with Lewis. Is this simply a reflection of the profusion of that flower on the island, or is there any further meaning:

After the bleakness of winter, any form of colour at all on Lewis would be more brilliant than in a place where the bleakness wasn't so prominent. Daffodils to me are associated with some kind of creativity, and the bleakness of the rock contrasted with some sort of life-force and colour can be striking.

If we could turn to 'Gaelic Songs', a poem which portrays Gaelic culture as at once valuable, fragile and threatened. This is a preoccupation that emerges elsewhere in your work. How do you feel about the concerns raised by the poem in the light of current interest in Gaelic through soap opera, Celtic rock bands, TV language programmes, Gaelic playgroups and so on?

I always used to find that if there had to be a cancellation on TV or radio because of some crisis, it was always the Gaelic programme that had to go and I would feel angry about it. How far Gaelic is now less vulnerable it's difficult to know. About 62,000 people said they knew Gaelic according to the last census, though what this actually means is hard to say. Does it mean that they can read Gaelic, or write it, or speak it?

What really encourages me more than anything else is not so much the money spent on Gaelic television as the amount of work that is being done with young people. A lot of Gaelic books are now being produced for young people and they are now able to go to school and instead of having to switch from Gaelic on the very first day, they learn some of their subjects in Gaelic and learn Gaelic in the classroom. These are things that are important and I think that what has happened with the figure of 62,000 (which is a drop on the previous one) is that Gaelic is now being concentrated at the younger levels whereas in the past it was mostly old people who were speakers of Gaelic. Now there's a real effort to catch the young people and that's important. Something I now do fairly regularly is to write Gaelic books for teenagers because this is one of the key areas that schools should be involved in. When we were at school we got 17th and 18th century Gaelic poetry and prose – nothing very relevant or new. Now Gaelic books are being published for people in their teenage years. I've done three such books and I'm currently working on another. I like doing these, as I feel young people shouldn't have to be bored when they're at school the way I was, because of the reading I had to do.

Related to this matter of contemporary Gaelic culture, the poem 'The TV' is structurally and tonally very different from the others. In some ways it's much lighter and more humorous but at the same time it does seem to be making a serious point.

Yes. I find television, apart from a few programmes here and there, a rather shallow medium. Some of the programmes aren't very interesting, particularly game shows and soap operas. I'm quite happy to see that, according to recent evidence, people are watching less television and going more to radio and buying books.

In a later television poem, 'TV', you return to these themes with increased seriousness and perhaps bitterness. Does this reflect a growing concern about television narratives and their effect on people's lives?

Yes, and one of the things one has to think about is the fact that television was actually quite destructive of the Gaelic language in my time. Now I think they have realised that it's important for young people to be given some idea of who they would want to be like so there's now more concentration on Gaelic television. How useful this will be I'm not sure, as I do find television rather superficial.

Coming back to your poetry as a whole, it's been said that your work is characteristically preoccupied with a rather bleak range of concerns: age, death, guilt and suffering. Do you think this is a fair generalisation?

Certainly my earlier poetry was concerned with these preoccupations because I came from a bleak island with an ageing population. When I was growing up in Lewis during the war years, which were my key years, there were many old people and only a few adolescents. I grew up on an island which has been on the periphery of events. But I think that my later poetry for the last two or three books has become more celebratory than my earlier work and I hope this will continue. I think the ageing population, a dying language, and a very strong religion which was in my opinion anti-life, were influences which were difficult to combat and I was trying to make sense of them.

One last question. In your autobiographical poem cycle 'A Life', your poems begin and end in Lewis, taking in various intermediate locations. Does Lewis continue to be a powerful presence in your work?

Not so much now. I had to work it out of my system and that book was a summing-up of the point I had reached at that time. I probably won't be going back so much to Lewis now, partly because I have no real relatives there any more and it changes such a lot. It was like a kind of problem I had to solve because I started off with two possible disadvantages as far as a writer in English was concerned: first of all I was on an island where my native language was Gaelic and I didn't learn English until I was five. Secondly, I was on an island which was quite strongly and powerfully religious. These were two things I had to work through and eventually I think I did work through them, especially the second one, the ideological force of the Church. I arrived at this position where I don't believe in any ideology at all and believe that all ideologies are harmful, that they must shut out whole areas of life in order to be a system. These are the kind of things I learned from Lewis. Probably now my writing can be more open, without any reference to Lewis at all.

Reading the 'Higher' Poems

Colin Nicholson

The inclusion of poems by Iain Crichton Smith as part of the Higher English curriculum presents us with an opportunity and a challenge. Not only is he one of the finest writers now producing in the anglophone world, but several aspects of representative Scottish experience come together in his poetry, giving it added resonance as a kind of cultural documentation and imaginative expression of the way we live. His work is tied to the local while perceptively interrogating the nature and significance of the web of connections and disconnections between personality and community. Educationally relevant in a variety of ways, by bringing into conjunction the function and interrelatedness of myth, memory, history and an often acutely personal perception of the ways that our senses of the present are shaped by the past, Crichton Smith's poetry invites us to examine forms of constancy and change in contemporary cultural values.

Because my concern here is with how the texts selected might be profitably encountered in the classroom, I propose to look individually at the poems chosen for curriculum inclusion, offering brief commentaries on each and indicating tactics and procedures of approach that might usefully lead on to further enquiry. Sartre suggests somewhere that the last act of the poem is the collective one of being read: I offer what follows as a possible first step in a process of participation that integrates and validates a body of writing for and within any community that may find what it has to say of relevance to its own individual and shared experience.

The poem 'Old Woman (and she, being old)' brings into play several topics and themes that recur in Crichton Smith's writing where the figure of the ageing female (often – though not exclusively, as this poem demonstrates – deriving from memories of the poet's own mother) becomes the subject of different treatments. In 'Old Woman' irony works to suggest the necessity of defensive mechanisms against the experience and perception being presented. There is something relentless and uncompromising in the opening comparison of a dying woman to an old mare feeding which implies that the description of God as "all-forgiving" ought not to be taken at face value. The angelic visitation prayed for by the caring husband has "foreign" wings because the strict island Calvinism that is repeatedly a religious context in this poetry does not recognise or acknowledge such things in its version of the Christian belief-system. And in the third stanza the speaker seems to acknowledge the inefficacy of such prayer when stormy winds displace an angry frustration at the inevitability of what is happening – "Outside, the grass was raging" – leaving him with feelings of pity and shame at what he is witnessing. To find other contexts for his feelings the speaker invokes the values of very different but equally rigorous and uncompromising belief-systems: those of Graeco-Roman antiquity where sanctioned termination of life would have been an appropriate response to senile dependency. But characteristically, this wished-for return to earlier cultural values is itself compromised and ambiguous: against the desire for these other codes of behaviour and response stands the description of the killing spear as "bitter".

Moving from Graeco-Roman modes of cognition back to more familiar Christian ones, the repetition of "he said" registers a futile duplication in the husband's prayer and contrasts with the starker "I saw" as the image of a death's-head skull is registered on the page. The poem is opening up for consideration relationships and differences between attitudes and ideas from classical antiquity and from the present and as it probes similarities and divergencies, it mingles pure with half-rhyme (or para-rhyme). The half-echo effect thus achieved conjures senses of semi-connection between rival modes of perception and apprehension. So the purer rhymes of the final stanza might be read as suggesting a kind of formal closure which the syntax works simultaneously to undermine. The poem is proposing its own uncompromising acknowledgement of finality *and* continuity as, picking up on the cyclical rising of "gradual crops" in the second stanza, it situates human transience in non-human patterns of recurrence, expertly catching the drag of an ebb-tide in "wishless seaweed" and linking it with the similar-yet-different "too", "to", and "two" of its final line.

In different mood, 'Two Girls Singing' remembers a night-time bus journey in November to celebrate the human voice. But within an apparent surface simplicity typical complexities are stirring, prompting questions about the mode of existence of music in both the human and non-human world and the nature and purpose of artistic accomplishment. Harmony, resilience and sheer delight in the unpredictable and unexpected are registered and celebrated, anticipating with relish vocal music's ambiguous dependency/independence between the oral and the aural, production with reception as, again, it plays with continuity and change. In those senses it usefully connects with 'At the Firth of Lorne' which places a speaker and his female partner on the Argyll coast at sunset looking westwards towards the islands to propose that nothing has changed and that "the world was as it was/ a million years ago."

But what is happening here, as so often in Crichton Smith's work, is that the nature of writing is itself brought under scrutiny, the process of producing a poem exposed to view, and the structure and function of myth and mythologies opened up for debate. The first stanza engages an emblematising process, hammering out in words its medallion image of golden sunlight on golden hair. The second stanza's geological metaphor of ferrous rock – "aboriginal iron" – combined with "slaty stone", sets a timescale which apparently diminishes the poem's human subjects: a timescale that lets us hear "perpetual" chime within the suggestion that the grass they are sitting on and looking out at will "perpetuate its sheep." The gap or distance between these dimensions of time and the human voices which so rapidly fade into silence is deftly registered before the closing lines of the poem imply the necessity of mythic structures which provide forms of continuity for otherwise transient human subjects:

> There was no tree
> nor other witness to the looks we gave
> each other there, inhuman as if tolled
> by some huge bell of iron and of gold,
> I no great Adam and you no bright Eve.

A paradisiacal or Edenic image of the Western Isles at sunset is compromised by the negative syntax which presents it – "no", "nor", "no" – with the speaker repudiating mythic identifications even as he gives them voice. The fateful "tree" of biblical mythology is absent as is any other satanic or angelic "witness" to the look these lovers exchange, and in these intensely human contexts it is the word "inhuman" that becomes paradoxical. Perhaps inhuman is being used to suggest that there is something here which, despite a semantic of denial, transcends the human, reaching beyond the immediacy of sensuous experience into other dimensions. If a myth of paradise is evoked in order to be negated, the structure of the poem will fashion a transcending permanence to preserve its human figures by making out of the sound and substance of its own preceding imagery a musical monument to the treasured moment. The earlier "brilliant gold" and "aboriginal iron" are now recomposed (retold?) to lend wider significance to those exchanged looks of love – "as if tolled/ by some huge bell of iron and of gold."

Certainly senses of a haunting and difficult-to-recover past are returning tropes in this poetry and 'At the Sale' constructs a metaphor of auction to explore feelings aroused by the reduction and flattening of a wealth and multiplicity of use-values to the blank monotony of an economy of exchange-value based upon a single scale of money-payment. Objects and possessions once resonant with human associations are now diminished to the status of merely purchasable artefacts, uprooted from the contexts which gave them purpose and place in personal and social patterns of signification. Against this process the poem asks a series of questions which momentarily restores to a welter of discrete, lifeless objects now up for sale their earlier participation in a human economy of use, memory and a once-affective network of relationships. And to emphasise this pervasive shift in values and disintegration of codes of valuation that once operated in determined and determining ways, an image of bibles (objects that repeatedly appear in Crichton Smith's writing) now up for auction brings to mind a vigorous ideology that once proclaimed its triumphal permanence against a rival scheme of belief that made the same kind of claim and assumption:

> The double-columned leather-covered tomes
> recall those praying Covenanters still
> adamant against Rome's
> adamant empire.

In the midst of these now-displaced objects, the poem produces an image of youth exposed to the passing of time:

> a boy in serious stance
> holds up a fan, a piece of curtaining,
> an hour-glass with its trickle of old sand.

The adult participants here, finding an object whose original purpose is unclear to them, treat it as a symbol of alienated labour endlessly repeated in an economy whose laws of transaction and exchange are never brought into question. A sad and wistful irony presents employees energetically committed to their task in "a happy country of anonymous laws", while the image of their retirement celebrations achieves a ghostly aspect as modernisation displaces earlier forms of work, a process of change in which both human transience and human redundancy are emphasised – "the flesh itself becomes unnecessary". To escape from these seeming inevitabilities the speaker seeks the comfort of his partner and the poem turns to a mattress now unused, a mirror that no longer reflects its erstwhile owner and, finally, a now-defunct instrument of communication and cultural participation. Describing the radio as "dismembered" nicely catches the sense of disintegrated purpose which forms part of the narrative here and perhaps also suggests "unmemoried", since unlike the human subjects that are involved, the broken radio "has no history" and is consequently untroubled by the reflections and disconnections here explored.

In his poem 'Lenin' Crichton Smith registers his resistance to any iron-bound philosophy or ideology, maintaining instead that "the true dialectic is to turn in the infinitely complex". It is a crucial utterance as far as his own writing practice is concerned where patterns of assumption and more emphatically any prescriptions and limitations placed upon individual understanding and response are vigorously, and sometimes scathingly opposed. When these libertarian and free-thinking impulses come up against constraining systems or myths of identification which mystify rather than clarify the realities of human experience, a provocative and sometimes disturbing poetry is produced. 'At the Highland Games' is caustic in its treatment of the distance that has opened up between Highland history and its contemporary representations and celebrations. Surface signs remain, but emptied, now, of earlier significations – "like re-reading a book which has lost its pith." Emblems and insignia which once held meaning and value decline into ritual and self-indulgence. Alcoholically red-faced participants are now imaged contemptuously as "meat with moustaches" and false romanticisations of the past, encoded in such tunes as the 'Skye Boat Song' deaden responses through meaningless repetition, evacuating the content of historic struggles: "The heroic dead die/ over and over the sea to misty Skye." But these ways of memorialising human endeavour also work to delete and displace from historical consciousness earlier subservience to systems of power. Given these unsettling meditations, the speaker's sense of the past is both reawakened and offended by what he sees and hears around him:

                                    I walk
among crew-cuts, cameras, the heather-covered rock,
past my ancestry, peasant, men who bowed
with stony necks to the daughter-stealing lord.

As a Gaelic speaker who now writes more in English than in his native tongue, Crichton Smith's relationship to subsequent developments in the romance of Highland origins is difficult and uneasy – "the Gaelic boils in my mouth" – and the poem closes on a note of contempt for the ways in which modern systems of representation – "stained pictures" – have displaced what was in fact aggressive – "raw, violent, alive and coarse" – by a coding of present violence which also disguises the reality of things:

I watch their heirs, Caligulas with canes
stalk in their rainbow kilts towards the dance.

But the senses of division and self-division which mark Crichton Smith's writing in regard to his fraught and distressing relationship with Gaelic appear in his writing in a variety of ways, and in a poem like 'Gaelic Songs' the uneven conflict between a metropolitan culture and its systems of communication and the marginalised voices of Gaeldom is given a disquieting airing. In a city environment these songs sound alien, their connectedness with a world of work, whether on boats of farms, becomes fractured. Cultural rootedness and durability is lost when Gaelic songs are broadcast to an audience less aware of their function in a distant and threatened community:

Now they are made of crystal
taking just a moment
between two programmes
elbowing them fiercely
between two darknesses.

These concerns also form the subject of 'The TV', scrutinising the effects modern media have upon those who are reduced to the role of passive observers. Here the displacement of values in an active and participatory culture results in a series of reductions: multifaceted experience is diminished into one-dimensionality. Nature is now refracted through a flat screen and while television can instruct its viewers about contemporary events, and prompt them to read books that have been televised, Plato's cave of poetry and imagination is transformed into an instrument of one-way transmission: Hollywood myths dislodge local heroes. When the television assumes such disproportionate significance, individual identity is jeopardised and we become estranged from ourselves, not knowing who or where we are. Finally, imprisonment within a technological cave is no longer recognised for what it is and the instrument of entrapment comes to be perceived as a mechanism of release.

It is hardly surprising, then, that Crichton Smith should more often turn his attention to the culture he was born into, even if the history of that culture seems marked as a story of relentless loss and deracination. Following the Clearances which began in the late eighteenth century and continued through the nineteenth, the depopulation of Gaelic territories continues into the present, motivated now by economic decline and the consequent pursuit of individual opportunities in other places. 'The Exiles' is one of several poems which explore this theme, and as so often in this writer's work, the treatment is deeply ambivalent. The poem's elegising tendency also carries a warning against any inclination to turn the sadness of these remembered events into a false consolation where nostalgia and regret are used as methods of escape from a disconsolate present, transformed into memories that are almost worshipped:

> like a plate on a wall
> to which they raise their hands
> like a silver magnet
> with piercing rays
> streaming into the heart.

Two poems which in different though related ways consider memories of the past to see what may usefully be recovered are 'You'll take a bath' and 'You lived in Glasgow'. In the first of these, an unremitting realism tempers and qualifies memories of childhood in cramped and unappealing urban conditions. But there are varied and even opposing registers at work here, suggesting a conflict of emotions in the imagination and memory of an adult narrator standing at his mother's grave and recalling their earlier life together, from his childhood onwards through subsequent separations. Story, fact and fantasy weave and unweave where images of knights in armour rescuing Rapunzel-like damsels imprisoned in distress collide with threatening graffiti, raucous radio music and sweating bodies: rival structures of feeling in the remembering narrator are being explored. The named door of his mother's flat in a high-rise urban tower block merges with the tombstone her surviving son is now looking at, these uncomfortable contrasts signifying the anguish still experienced by a memory that refuses to romanticise past and present actualities despite the evident pressure in the mind to do so. In these divisive contexts, the poem's closing reference to the graveyard willow's "maternal stance" seems poor recompense for the absent mother.

That same absent figure haunts the narrative of 'You lived in Glasgow' where the psychology of personal loss mingles with divergent senses of cultural rootedness and individual displacement. Crichton Smith was born in Glasgow but moved to the island of Lewis where he grew up and this poem explores among other things the twin difficulties of recalling past relationships – "I do not find your breath in the air" – and of reconstituting memory and history – "The past's an experience that we cannot share". Against the seductive attractiveness of viewing what is now gone within the false comfort of a nostalgic afterglow, the verse sets a characteristic and undermining realism – "The sparkling Clyde/ splashing its local sewage at the wall". The compromised and uncertain survival of private recollections contrasts with the evident durability of Glasgow's urban statuary; but although "the mottled flesh is transient" and never to be reconstituted in actuality, memory and affection have their own mode of survival, their own patterns of continuity:

> There is no site for the unshifting dead.
> You're buried elsewhere though your flickering soul
> is a constant tenant of my tenement.

Where urban renewal and improvement also results in lost contexts, eradicated environments, the poem works hard to resist its own tendency to embalm its memories in sentimental recuperation. Glasgow's history and present has harsher reality to contend with: the soccer rivalry between Celtic and Rangers both masks and exposes sometimes violent religious antagonisms in a "divided city of the green and blue".

So the problematic encounters of 'You lived in Glasgow' inscribe oppositions and relationships between permanence and transience, change and continuity, between the present and the past, the personal and the political, the existential and the cultural. The returning voice here, back in the city and negotiating his own complex responses also records a wider sense of cultural loss – "my constant aim/ to find a ghost within a close who speaks/ in Highland Gaelic". 'The Exiles' had imaged the survival of Gaelic song among the departing sailors who were effectively depopulating the territory which had first sustained that music – "in their masts sailors singing/ like birds on branches." At the close of 'You lived in Glasgow' this attenuated survival is further jeopardised as the slums of the 1930s give way to the high-rise blocks of the 1970s and forms of renewal bring with them forms of cultural transformation:

> Boyish workmen hang
> like sailors in tall rigging. Buildings sail
> into the future. The old songs you sang
> fade in the pop songs, scale on dizzying scale.

Recognitions of inevitability in Crichton Smith's poetry contend with forms of resistance, and its responses to change and continuity are subtle and complex. Even a lifelong hostility to the repressive and life-denying prescriptiveness of the island Calvinism he came to know so well on Lewis can find space for a kind of admiration for their single-mindedness of purpose, as 'A Note on Puritans' makes clear. But one of the attractive constancies in his own writing is his inventive determination to set the richness of his own visions of life's plural and multifaceted possibilities against the monocular poverty of restricted and restrictive religious ideology. 'The Law and the Grace' is an effective expression of the sometimes intolerable pressures exerted against the artistic life by adherents to Calvinism both jealous of their own exclusive claims to ideological dominance and prohibitively suspicious of any imaginative exploration of alternative modes of being for imaginative free-thinking. In this respect, the poem 'Iolare' is a striking if disturbing attempt at empathic engagement with the thought processes of a church elder on Lewis confronted with what Crichton Smith's note on the poem calls a "mind-breaking" disaster. On New Year's Eve in 1918 a ship called the *Iolare*, bringing three hundred men back home to Lewis after four years' war service, went aground. About two hundred men died and through the construction of a Free Church elder's monologue Crichton Smith attempts to come to terms with his own difficulty in imagining a God who, if he could control anything at all, would allow so many people to be drowned on their own island on New Year's morning after they had spent four years in the war. One of the poem's achievements is the maintenance of a tone that apparently acquits the minister in terms of his own vocalised response until the closing lines release the possibility that the only genuine reaction to what has happened is for the speaker to abandon his faith and achieve a kind of calm by drowning himself. But as the poem opens, the bland responses it registers condemn themselves as hopelessly inadequate to the tragedy that has occurred. From describing the event as "an enigma", the several repetitions of "seemed" marks a retreat from actuality, and the "sloppy" waves and "fat" of water register more as a critique of this kind of thinking than as a description of tidal movements. And self-condemnation is further emphasised when the minister's question to his God "have we done ill" is followed by the image of his own "fixed body/ a simulacrum of the transient waste". There are powerful feelings stirring here, simultaneously suppressed within the minister's monologue and yet breaking through as an angry and painful sub-text in the poem's wider effects: drowned bodies imaged as "bruising against their island", subsequently become the "bruised blue" of the sea when daybreak's "remorseless amber" touches the "erupting edges" of the waves. A dawning sense of the inadequacy of a Calvinist vision of God as "the black thunderer from the hills" develops into a hell-fire image when the minister touches one of the corpses – "my hand is scorched". And this undercurrent of withdrawal from customary religious response to God is again registered when the expected preposition is replaced to produce a shock of dislocation on the minister's part – "I kneel from you". It then comes to "seem" appropriate, although the poem does not state this explicitly, that the minister escapes from the "ache above [his] globular eyes" by joining the bodies he sees around him: "I am embraced/ by these green ignorant waters. I am calm."

There is of course much more that can be said about these poems and my intention here has been only to suggest preliminary approaches, 'ways in' to the texts that might diversify and proliferate in different directions through classroom analysis and debate. But there is a final suggestion I would like to make. Crichton Smith is a writer of hugely various talent, and although it would be a mistake to think that his comic spirit is never evident in his verse, it is true that he can be hilariously funny in other forms. There is an excellent selection of his short stories published in the Canongate Classics series, called *Listen to the Voice*. I recommend that copies be bought for school libraries, and teachers interested in bringing this work to the attention of a wider audience could do worse than persuade their students to start with 'Napoleon and I'. It's a riot.

Colin Nicholson

SCOTLAND
ALBA

SALTIRE
SOCIETY

Mirror and Marble

The poetry of Iain Crichton Smith

Carol Gow

In this comprehensive survey of Crichton Smith's poetry, Dr Carol Gow offers a new and challenging view, that after forty years' poetic development Crichton Smith has reached a threshold and has now passed into a new phase.

ISBN 0 86334 070 9 £8.95
The Saltire Society: Lines Review Editions

Towards the Human

Iain Crichton Smith

These essays are here collected for the first time, and reflect the author's interests and concerns, especially about Gaelic and the threat to Gaelic culture. Other essays include pieces on Hugh MacDiarmid, George Bruce and Robert Garioch.

ISBN 0 86334 059 8 £7.95
The Saltire Society: Lines Review Editions

An Guth Aoibhneach
(The Joyful Voice)

Sgeulachdan le
Pol MacAonghais

Paul MacInnes (Pòl MacAonghas) was brought up in Uist, where he became a fluent Gaelic speaker. From 1979 he was a Gaelic producer for the BBC, scripting many programmes. Before he died in 1987 he became well-known for his Gaelic short stories, many of which appeared in magazines or were anthologised. They have not, however, been collected previously. This selection comprises 18 stories ranging from the 1950s to the 1980s, and in style from the comic to the tragic.

ISBN 0 85411 054 2 £8.95
The Saltire Society

The Saltire Society, 9 Fountain Close, 22 High Street, Edinburgh EH1 1TE

Iain Crichton Smith

The legend

The stones and the leaves and the sun are separate.
I put them together, I weave a legend,

and Odysseus comes into it, and his tall black dog,
and his speech to the peasants who do not understand it,

and the tapestry (unfinished) hanging down from the day
and the experience he hasn't had is Death,

and there is a man in black walking about the island,
in a whirlpool of light, and he is saying, There is only one God,

and Odysseus sets out one evening of surpassing redness
with his old friends, his hands scorched by the oars,

and they drown somewhere where the sun is a red fire,
and while he is drowning there is Penelope

in front of her painting of stones, leaves, and the sea
and she is singing quietly, for nothing is ever done.

Let me gather

Let me gather round me the few objects
that I'd take with me to another land.
Firstly, my pen which is my finger's claw.
Secondly, the paper, ghostly white,
but a clear sky in which my skylarks sing.
Thirdly, I think a tall graceful vase
around which time might beat uselessly
and the waves reflect from.
                    Also, a thin wrist watch
to be the sparkling master of the day.
None of my books of course and no fiction,
just fact on fact clear as the blue hills,
and no philosophy, certainly none of that.
I'd grow to love my chair, and the dear water,
and the knife I'd carve a knotty table out of,
just as much as the stars that bowed down
their lofty jewellery over my Azed crossword.

Some people

Some people escape history
and are without name

like, who opened the door
for Napoleon
before he stepped towards Waterloo:
or who in the zoo
of lineages
stood behind a chair
while a great king
was poisoned:

or who in the wind
of cavalry passing
saw a hoof strike a stone
in the cloaked shadow
of mud-strewn Wellington.

Snowdrop

Without ancestry
the snowdrop on the Highland hill emerges

without the surges
of a broken soldiery,

or the stench
of a burning house,

white and delicate,
nosing like a deer

the wind without a name:
see, it appears,

so vulnerable,
without weapons

asserting so shyly
its place among stones.

Once, and now

Once there was a ladder, now is not,
a crystal set of boxes, nests of stars,
Ptolemy's local absolute jewellery.

Then such explosions! We were blown into
seas and space, and the ladder fell
and shattered among the rabbits and the snakes.

Millions of selves shone starkly: millions of eyes
were wildcats of the universe. Now it is

a wall-less house that seems to be our home
extended all ways, ourselves giving us welcome.

Nothing absolute

Nothing absolute
ever stepped out of nature,
not even a lion
with its awesome face:
for no laws
were scribbled on the stone
that the rain washes:
and no estates were claimed
to all eternity
by the scythe-beaked eagle.

Ireland

When you come from Ireland
it is strange that there is no blood on your sleeve,
it is strange that Ireland still exists
with all its persistent jabberings.

Like a mechanism that will not shut up
and which grinds its people like a butcher,
that country that was emerald green
but will not cease arguing.

A demented ancient mumbling country
whose bullets explode in the fire,
and the lakes are like dead eyes
and black hoods bless bloody coffins.

Dogma

When you have scythed
a space from the rich
cornfield, and you stand
there alone,

crying, this is
the world, and the
meaning of the world:
and the perfumes

waver elsewhere.
This is the bare
area where I plant
my fixed tent.

The sun shines
on it, the moon
and the many
stars:

all rays are
directed from it.
No wind
will shake it down.

Its laws
do not wave
like the breeze
in the corn,

they are in fact
like stones. Stones
indeed are its
facts. And also

my scythe is ready
to cut the colour
of lies which loom
from the adjacent swish.

One light falls
on it undiluted:
and the girls
who pass by it,

laughing, are hauled
into it by the hair
which must be sheared
by the smart scissors

of our caretakers.
O love it,
love this land,
love every implement

and tradition,
lest you should fall
into the dizzying swish
of the hateful

neighbouring parish
of carefree gold.
All has been foretold
by this shining scythe.

The robot

Dressed as a robot
in a white suit
this jerky man
in the East Kilbride precinct
is raising money
for the Somalia children.

We cannot see him
behind his flour-white suit
and his mechanical motions,
exactly like a robot,
while the awed children bring him
their sweaty mites.

O children of Somalia
this is your white god,
as if with jerky nerves
clock-like, distraught,
a surgical and masked
benevolent robot,

in this flourishing precinct
almost imitant of your
almost destroyed structures:
my dear friendly robot
who shakes like a flawed god,
precise and distant.

The Wind

Iain Crichton Smith

It was an autumn of high winds, and the house that he had taken for three weeks was perched on a headland facing the sea. The area was more desolate than he had imagined it would be. There were the straggling houses of the village about half a mile away; and a little shop which sold miscellaneous stuff, and was also a post office.

His father had always told him of the close community that existed in the village, but it was hard to visualise it. During the day the village looked quiet and almost dead: the few children were back in school. "Songs and dances," his father would say, "what we called ceilidhs": and his face would shine with the memories of them. Of course, the place would look better in fine weather: perhaps he should have come in June or July.

Naturally, the villagers knew he was here, and who he was. But his father's generation was dead, and the middle-aged people like himself were not hospitable in the old way. Some of the houses were surprisingly fine, indeed impressive; there were of course no thatched houses left, not even their ruins. The fields here and there held wrecks of abandoned cars.

Why had he come here in the first place from South Africa? Sheila naturally wouldn't come.

"You can go," she had said, "but I don't see any need for all this pseudo-nostalgia." One certainly couldn't call her sentimental. She hadn't, for instance, gone home when her father and mother had died, with a short interval between them, in Dunoon. She had always travelled light.

Yet he had always wanted to see this world that his father had told him about. It had sounded like a sort of paradise, carefree and generous.

The people cared for each other, helped each other, his father would say. Yet in the post office he had heard them complain of "white settlers", and he had gathered that there was a Dutch family in the village as well as English ones. "They come here, and drive the price of property up, and the young people can't afford to buy a house."

He had gone to see the croft on which his father had grown up. ("Plenty of milk and crowdie.") But there was no sign of the original home, and a large new house had been built in its place.

No one had invited him to visit. He had been able to rent the house he was in for three weeks while the owners were on holiday: they did Bed & Breakfast in the summer, and autumn was the time when they took their break. They had in fact gone to Malta.

It was a nice house with all the modern conveniences that he had in his own home in Johannesburg, except of course that there was no swimming pool. But then who would use a swimming pool in weather like this? In fact, he felt cold a good deal of the time: and he missed the colour of the jaracanda trees. There were no trees here at all, and little colour. The wind swept over desolate bleak moorlands, and the sea looked sullen and strong.

He read most nights or watched television. Certainly he rested, though in fact he didn't need much rest. He had his own accountancy business, and it was successful enough. Whatever stress he felt was not because of the business but because of what was happening in the country generally. There had been a large number of murders in Johannesburg.

Though his father had been briskly kind to the blacks, he had a profound contempt for them. To him they were stupid, careless, childlike and dilatory. Sometimes he would say that there had been people like that in the village where he had grown up on the island. That was why he had joined the police in Glasgow, and later emigrated to South Africa where he had been manager of a diamond mine.

Angus himself didn't think like his father: he was much more confused, far less definite in his opinions. He sensed danger and potential chaos: an office not far from his own had been blown up in the middle of the day: buses too had been blown up. The biblical certainties that his father had recognised in South Africa were not so strong among his own generation.

We made this country, his father would say, though he had in fact been an incomer. Still, South Africa was different from Rhodesia, it didn't have so many fly-by-nights who fled when the going got rough.

What troubled him here was the incessant wind. It had a curious keening sound almost as if it spoke of all the exiles who had left the island. He found it piercing and melancholy, especially when he was sitting at night trying to relax with a book. He had never heard this kind of wind before. It bothered him for some reason that he couldn't understand.

He had time to think a great deal in this strange and almost alien environment. He thought of his father setting off on the boat to Glasgow. He thought of Sheila handing round drinks to their friends on a fine evening when the sun was setting. Sheila wouldn't have his father to stay with them when he had his stroke. He must go to a home instead.

"Can you imagine me lifting him?" she had said contemptuously. "I have more to do with my time", though in fact she hadn't, since she hadn't worked since their wedding. She had been a secretary in a law firm. Angus had felt guilty about his father, who had for some unaccountable reason reverted to speaking in Gaelic after his stroke: he himself had no Gaelic.

Yet it was probably true that Sheila wouldn't have been able to cope: it wasn't so much that, it was the decisive manner in which she had spoken, like his own father almost. There was no hesitation: and in fact she hadn't visited him much in the Home.

"I don't understand that weird language", she would say. And that was it, the language thereupon dismissed as having no use and no meaning.

She had a firm belief that there would be no fundamental changes in South Africa. She would remain mistress of her servants: the regime would last her lifetime and perhaps for ever.

Yet he himself knew perfectly well, as an accountant, that this wasn't right. Businesses weren't doing well: and even the business community had begun to talk of the harmfulness of apartheid. The blacks had begun to use economic weapons against their masters: boycotts of shops, strikes.

The day he had been to Stornoway, a little while after the loss of £23 million in the débàcle of BCCI, he had felt a certain familiarity in the scene. The people looked stunned, disbelieving, angry. The outside world had struck at them savagely. They could no longer be protected by seas and tradition. And anyway what was their council doing dealing with a bank that was connected with drugs: even their religious feelings had been shaken. Also, roads and schools could not be built now. There would be more poverty, more constriction. Just as in South Africa when the sanctions had been initiated. No one was isolated now: it was all a vast web: if you tugged one part of it the whole structure would vibrate. A minister had preached that it was the will of God. Such complexity, along with such naïvité!

He didn't think much of Stornoway itself. It was a grey little fishing town and yet for his own father it had been a metropolis. He would say to him, "We used to visit Stornoway once a year when I was young. I remember the smell of apples, and the ice-cream."

Here the people didn't seem to care whether he was a South African or not, unlike London where a bearded fellow had suddenly, hearing his accent, lashed out at him verbally. "What about your police?" he had shouted, "Fascists, the lot of them. What about the black suicides in jail? Butchers, Nazis, bloody sadists." And all the while he himself had remained calm, though shaken by the depth of the man's hatred. A bearded, literary-looking man suddenly raging at him in a bookstall.

From what he could gather, there was a lot of sympathy on the island for the white South African. Bible-thumping Protestants together?

It was the wind however that troubled him. Sometimes at night he couldn't sleep because of its high wailing sound. It was almost like the cry of an abandoned child: it seemed to have a human quality. It spoke of an infinite pain, of a tremendous heartbreaking loss. And there was no community here that he could see. Perhaps there had been in his father's time. Perhaps it had something to do with the thatched houses that his father had talked about.

He rose from his chair. It was dark outside and the sea was a deep black apart from the light cast by a moon careering among the clouds as if out of control. Now and again the windows of the house would shake. It seemed to him that he could see his father's white disordered face after the stroke. Of course he had led a very hard, diligent life: he had also been a strict disciplinarian.

"Why can't you make up your mind?" Sheila would shout at him. "Why can't you be more like your father?" But how could he be like his father? He was not, for instance, religious. But there was an absence that he had become more and more aware of, and that was why perhaps he had come to the island. If only that bloody whining wind would stop!

His health was good and so was Sheila's, and so was Rosemary's. Rosemary was doing well as a teacher in a Pietermaritzburg school: a private school, in leafy surroundings, where she had once been a pupil.

He had bought a copy of the local paper. On the letter page a correspondent had gone on at great length about Sunday Observance: while another gave a religious reason for the financial collapse. There was an elaborate scenario, on a news page, about whether litter should be removed from the streets on Sunday even in the face of a mandatory law. In a curious way it reminded him of South African fundamentalism. Draw back into the laager while the wind howls around you! Hope that the storm will pass!

He remembered a story his father had told him. He had once been home on holiday in the island and he had bought a van for a nephew of his, so that he could sell fish. Earning a lot of money for the first time in his life, the nephew had taken to drink and had smashed up the van. Then he had run away from home, taken a job on the mainland and married his landlady, who was much older than him.

A kaffir, Angus's father had called him, nothing but a kaffir. Of course the boy's mother had been angry and had blamed him for the disaster. But it wasn't his fault: he had only been trying to help. "I also bought her a washing machine," his father said, "but she never used it; she would rather gossip with her neighbour at the washing line."

On his own on the island, Angus thought about a lot of things. About Sheila, for instance, and her extremely rightist views and her mishandling of the servants. Even his father had complained about her tactlessness. There were some things she was incapable of learning. It was a question of knowing from the inside what to do, what not to do. There was no reason why one shouldn't be kind to one's servants, his father would say. But she had always been brusque and contemptuous. And in argument she was the same, ignorant and aggressive, uninterested in finding common ground. Nevertheless she was still beautiful – when he had first met her, astonishingly so: blonde and tall and high-boned, long-legged and blue-eyed, a secretary such as one might see in a television advertisement.

"There are certain ways of doing things", his father would mutter angrily. He didn't seem to know how to deal with Sheila's beauty, and her essentially cruel and crude beliefs.

Still, there was no question but that the blacks could at times be irritating. He himself had offered a rise in wages to one of the servants, and the servant had immediately left on the grounds that he had been cheated, that he should have had the money from the beginning. What could you make of such economic thinking?

Really, what was he doing here? He paced restlessly about the living room. In a bookcase there were volumes by Alasdair Maclean, Jack Higgins, Frederick Forsyth. There were no Gaelic books that he could see, except for a rather old bible with a black cover. It wasn't actually all that different from a house in South Africa with its big round globe in which there were bottles of vodka, gin and whisky. On the walls and sideboards there were many photographs, mostly of young children.

"When we were children," his father would say, "we would fish for eels in the rivers and pick blaeberries on the moors."

That bloody whining wind! He was beginning to feel that it was a constant unavoidable universal noise. He couldn't explain what he felt about it; it was like a ghostly permanent dirge that never stopped, as if it were composed of many voices in concert. A wind at the end of the world, among these ancient stones. It seemed to be saying to him, What are you doing here? You are a stranger, you are an interruption to this wind of death.

He made himself a cup of coffee and sat staring into the electric fire. "They sit and stare into the fire", his father had said. "They say they have all kinds of sicknesses and diseases, but it's all laziness. They need a good shake." And his face would redden with rage and high blood pressure. "Our history, they say, what can we do? And they whine and whine. I bought a set of false teeth for my sister Chrissie but she wouldn't wear them."

Here I am on the edge of things, he thought, as if I was at the Cape; this house shaky and shivering, and the sea below the headland black as tar, heaving and swelling, and monotonously stormy.

White houses these are known as, he thought, as distinct from black houses; that was what his father had told him. The black houses were the thatched ones: and in them the fire was in the middle of the floor, and it was in them also that the ceilidhs took place.

When people moved into the white houses, it was different, his father had said. Somehow the fire in the middle of the floor made a difference.

That woman in South Africa in a rural area who had found her husband's head hung in a tree like a strange fruit!

The wind was rising to a shriek, as if it were demented. He couldn't take much more of this. Maybe it hadn't been a good idea, after all, coming here. My father romanticised the place because it was connected with a relatively carefree childhood. But that was long before they had lost their £23 million, before the intricate outside world had impinged on them, whether they liked it or not. Bloody fools, he thought sourly, from his knowledge of accountancy, putting all their money in one bank like that. Bloody idiots. But South Africa could not insulate itself from the wide world either. The famous treks had probably been sentimentalised too. The bible-wielding patriarchs would crack as the sea eventually breaks rocks.

And people would hear that whine, they would no longer be able to shut it out. It would shake orange trees, jaracarandas. It would blow and blow, and the voices of the dead would be heard in it: the voices of the dying and the living. Even Sheila would eventually hear it, among her cosmetics and her vodkas and gins. Infinite eternal whining wind!

"My mother and father died on the island when I had just come to South Africa", his father told him. "I couldn't afford to go home at that time." And later Sheila wouldn't go home to her father's funeral. She had despised him. He had never made anything of himself, and he boasted to the neighbours that she was married to a very rich man. "She's never had to work since she got married", he would say, leaning on his stick. He was always whining about what the world had done to him. During the war he had been wounded in both legs. She couldn't forgive him his bad luck: he had wanted to visit them but she wouldn't have it.

He looked at a picture hanging on a wall of the living room. It showed a woman carrying peats in a creel: she was knitting as she walked along.

No, he couldn't stay here. He would pay for the full three weeks, but he would leave the island as soon as possible. If he couldn't get a plane he would stay in London, among people.

All night the wind continued, and he could hardly sleep. Sometimes he thought it was a voice trying to speak to him in Gaelic: perhaps his father after his stroke. Sometimes he thought it came from inside himself and that would be the worst of all; that would be madness.

The following day he locked everything carefully behind him and abandoned the white house. The sea was still turbulent and black. The houses crouched against the rocky ground like seashells. As he drove away from the village in the blue car he had hired in Stornoway, he said, "Goodbye, Father." And, whistling, to keep out that whine, he headed towards the town from which he would get the boat that would take him to the mainland and on the first stage of his homeward journey.

Crìsdean Whyte

bho *An Trath Duilich*

1 Nach neònach an eileamaid tìm.

Tha dòigh an uisge aice.

An àiteannan ruithidh i gu soilleir, glan,
neo-ghlacmhor; ach an àiteannan eile
gheibhear air reothadh i,
sìorraidh, gun iochd,
gach dùil ri aiteamh air chall.

Chithear san òg-mhadainn i
mar smodanachd san àile,
a' faighinn corporrachd le maille
nach urrainn do neach a ghiùlan,
mar boinneachan de dhriùchd a thèid a chrochadh
air fad nam meanganan neo-sgeadaichte
nan clagain bheaga, fhìnealta,
a bhristeas le co-sheirm neo-fhaicsinneach.

Ach tha àiteannan eile ann
far an deach sruthadh tìm a bhacadh,
's i fàs na lùnndaire,
a' sìneadh a-mach, a' doimhneachadh, a' màirneal.

Chaisgeadh luath-ghàir a rèis.
Thugadh dearbh-fhios dha na fuarain
am fionnarachd a bhith gun fheum.
Thrèig na min-èisg lainnireach
an linne dhuaichnidh, is eagal orra
ro na bha 'm falach anns na sgàilean fàsmhor.

Dh'atharraich na lusan reamhar slaodach
('s iad air a bheathachadh aig eabar maoth
an aigeinn) prìomh-bhlas grad-allt nan slèibh,
a' sgaoileadh mìlse mheallt' am brèine
's an lobhaidh leisgeil fhèin mun cuairt.

Trobhad a-nis, is feuchamaid
an tèid an gàrradh-sprùillich a leagail sìos,
am fairtlich e oirnn sruth an aonaich luim
a shlànachadh bhon ghalar sin
a mhùch e is a thruaill e.

2 Tha iomadh fàileadh sgreamhail ann.

Preas nach deach a sgioblachadh o chionn fhada,
seòmar is an còmhnaiche gun uinneag

Christopher Whyte

from The Difficult Time

1   *Time is a strange element*
It's like water.

In places it runs clear and bright,
elusive, but in other places
it's frozen,
pitiless, eternal,
without any hope of thaw.

You can see it in the early morning
like moisture in the air,
condensing with unbearable
slowness in dewdrops
hung along bare twigs,
small, fragile bells
that shatter with invisible resonance.

But in other places still
time's flow was blocked,
it grew sluggish, spilled over,
loitering and getting deeper.

All its exultant speed was checked.
Springs were told in no uncertain terms
that their freshness was no longer needed.
The gleaming small fry left the ugly pool,
afraid of what was hidden
in its gathering shadows.

The fat, dragging plants feeding
on the soft mud of the bottom
changed the water's flavour
of rushing hillside streams,
and spread the sweet, deceptive rottenness
of their own putrefaction through it.

Come, let's see if we can break
the dam of rubbish down
and heal this stream, that comes from bare
moorlands, of the sickness
that's suffocating and polluting it.

2   *Lots of things have loathsome smells.*

A cupboard not cleaned out for ages,
a room whose inmate rarely opens

fhosgladh ach gu tearc, am mathachadh
a shìneas iad a-mach sna h-achaidhean
as t-fhoghar, aodach air a chàrnadh suas
a dh'fhan ro fhada ris an inneal-nighe,
cac nan con a bheir thu leat san taigh
air bonn do bhròige, braidhmean do choin fhèin,
sgeitheadh naoidhein an dèidh dhà a bhiadh a ghabhail
nach robh ùin' agad a ghlanadh a-mach gu h-iomlan,
's a nochdas tu an ath-latha air do lèine,
breuntachd gobhla nach fhac' ach gann an siabann.

Ach is sgreamhail thar gach sgreamhalachd,
gràineal thar gach uile fhàileadh gràineil
fàileadh an àite sin.

19 Dh'fhalbh an luchd-seallaidh. Chaidh
na solasan, ach cuid a-mhàin, a mhùchadh.
Tha dorchadas air teàrnadh anns an taigh-
cluich a bha cho fuaimneach, cho làn
thograidhean is dèanadais.
Thrèigeadh e, ach cha do leigeadh
sìos an cùirtean, dh'fhan na h-actairean
gun ghluasad air an ùrlar-cluich,
balbh is rag san dorchadas. Seall!
Tha iad cho beag 's gun tog mi iad
gu furasda, fear seach fear, nam làimh,
chan eil annt' ach pùpaidean,
dathte, èibhinn, na sagartan,
Iosa, am maighstir-sgoil, na balaich bheag',
an rìgh, am prìosanach, mo mhàthair fhèin
(glacaidh mi i, chan eil maothachd innte,
direach, 's ann bho fhiodh a rinneadh i).
Cha bhi a' chluiche seo agam tuilleadh.
Càirichidh mi gu socair anns a' bhogsa
gach fear dhiubh, ach tha 'n diabhal air teicheadh
– an crochair! Am fairtlich e orm an còmhnaidh
e fhèin a ghlacadh? Siud e, ma-tha. Shèid mi
às a' choinneal, cha do dh'fhàgadh ach
cùbhraidheachd a mùchaidh, is an t-sàmhchar
seo, is i cho torrach, labhairteach.

20 A leannain m' òige, ciamar a dhealachainn riut?
Thug thu uiread a lèonadh dhomh, ach bha
suim mhòr agam eadhon sna leòntan sin.
Is urrainn don àmhghar a bhith na saoghal fhèin,
's ma bhitheas mi ga cur air falbh, an e
an aonranachd a bhios agam mar dhàn?

the window, the manure they spread
on the fields in autumn, clothes piled up
that have waited too long for the washing machine,
dog shit you brought into the house
on the sole of your shoe, your own dog's fart,
a baby's vomit when it's been fed
you hadn't time to clean off properly
and find on your shirt the morning after,
the stink of a crotch that rarely sees soap.

But loathsome beyond all loathsomeness,
more repulsive than any repulsive smell
is the odour of that place.

19 The audience has gone. All but
a few of the lights have been put out.
Darkness fills the theatre that was
so noisy, so alive with actions and passion.
It's empty now, but the curtain hasn't
come down yet. The actors are still standing
motionless on the stage, dumb
and rigid in the darkness. Look!
They're so small I can pick them up
easily, one by one, in my hand,
they're nothing but marionettes, brightly coloured,
amusing, the priests, Jesus, the headmaster,
the little boys, the king, the prisoner,
my mother (I catch her, there's no softness there,
I was forgetting she's made of wood).
I won't play that game ever again.
I'll put them away carefully in their box,
each one, but the devil has disappeared –
the rascal! Am I never to track
him down? That's it, then. Now I blow
the candle out, there's nothing left
but the fragrance of its extinction,
and this silence, so fruitful, full of words.

20 Lover of my youth, how can I part with you?
You hurt me so much, but even those
wounds were precious to me.
Pain can make a world of itself,
and if I reject it, is
only loneliness left?

Is e an cùram as motha th' ormsa
nach mair thusa an dèidh dhomh a bhith gad thrèigsinn.
Is e a tha sna muladan 's na meamhairean
dòigh air an dorchadas a lìonadh
le sluagh, co-dhiù. Ach chaidh e às an fhasan.
Chan urrainn dhomh do chuideachadh nas mò.

An Deidh a' Bhlair

Thuit a' phlangaid ròmach beagan sìos
is oisinn dhith a' suathadh ris a' chlogaid
a chuir thu dhiot, le suaicheantas na h-Aithne,
faisg ri do chuarain 's t' armachd air an ùrlar.
Chaidh cuimireachd do ghuailnean fhoillseachadh
tha lùthmhor fhathast nan cadal, sgaoil grian chiùin
an earraich ùir a lainnir thar do chraicinn
agus tha èirigh riaghailteach do bhroillich
far a bheil fuilteanan na stùr de dh'òr
a' saoradh t' analach cùbhraidh feadh na teanta
's i coimeasgta ri brèin an fhallais nach
do nigheadh bho do chorp as dèidh an strì.
Na bi iomagain ort! Chlisg thu, an t-eagal
a' nochdadh na do shùilean. Chan eil ann
ach mise, manadh òigeir a mharbh thu
an-diugh an teas na còmhraige. Seall orm!
Tharraing m' fhuil-sa abhainn eadar-fhight'
thairis air map an t-slèisd bho leòn no shlios
's e fàs cruaidh 's ag atharrachadh a dhath.
Chaill mi an làmh cho sùbailt' leis an dèanainn
rèidh mo dhubh-fhalt bachlagach, is chuir
saighdear-cois sàil gharg a bhròig rim ghruaidh
an oillt an ruaig, a dhuaichneachadh na gnùis
cho soinneanta a dheàlraich romhad san tiota
a thog thu 'n ball-airm agad airson mo bhualadh.

Ach sguir ded chaoineadh. Eirich, till don bhlàir;
an dèidh dhut mo chorp a lorg 's a sgioblachadh
nigh e, tog air do ghualann e, is falbh
a theampall 's e falaicht' an dos air leathad a' ghlinn.
Tha pailteas dhiathan fhathast beò, 's ar saoghal
làn drùidheachd sheòlta, riamh nach aom. Bha dia
crom air an leabaidh far an deach mo bhreith
is shèid e cuid de mhìorbhail fhèin nam bhith.
'S dòcha gun tig ath-bheòthachadh nam chorp
's gum faigh thu, 'n àite thaibhse nì do thathaich
leannan a bhith ga tharraing dhut 'son pòig.

What worries me most is that you
will stop existing if I abandon you.
Sorrows and memories are at least
a way of peopling the darkness.
But it's gone out of fashion.
I can do nothing more for you.

After the Battle

The rough blanket has slipped down
and a corner rubs against the helmet
with its Athenian plumes you placed
by your sandals and breastplate on the ground.
Vigorous still in sleep, your finely moulded
shoulders are revealed, the gentle sun
of spring has burnished your skin,
hairs are a dross of gold on your chest
which, in its regular rise and fall,
sends your fragrant breath through the tent
to mix with the smell of sweat you didn't
wash from your body after the battle.

Don't be afraid! You started, fear
glanced in your eyes. It's only me,
the ghost of a young man you killed
at the height of the fighting today.
Blood from the wound in my side has drawn
an intricate river down the map of my hip:
it's hardening and changing colour now.
I've lost the supple hand I used
to smooth my curly black hair with,
and in the panic of flight an infantry soldier
stove in with his heel the serene cheek
that gleamed in front of you
just as you raised your weapon to strike.

Stop crying. Get up, go to the field,
look for my body, tidy it, and wash it,
then lift it on your shoulder and take it
to a temple hidden in the woods above the valley.

Many gods are still alive; our world
is rich in a cunning magic that won't fade.
A god bent over the bed where I was born
and breathed something of his wonder into me.
Maybe life will come back to my body
and instead of a ghost to haunt you
you'll have a lover to draw to you and kiss.

Harvey Holton

Extracts from 'The Wuid Tink'

2   Whaur the nakit wunds derk edge sterts
amin fawin pine needles an taiglt brainches,
whaun the green licht o Venus owre the lift smerts
A'm tae be fund in derk peaty trenches
gaitherin the richt makins o the brew.

Or in the steam hoose singin watter oan het stane
for veesions baith prophetic an true;
wie birk bark an toadstool through oo A strain
tae daunce, daunce again the reel o time
as bear an tod, eagle, wolf an brock.

Lissen, lissen noo tae the sternies rhyme,
the daylicht dwams o bairnies that rock
the yird oan its pinnacle garrin it shak
the harns o awe the wild baists in its stock
sae that A noo maun see the things A mak.

5   The braw blae o Homer's lift
lowes bricht as wir tears
that in cut rainforests shift
the mud an gitters o a thoosan years
whaur growin, connectit, life
its ain wild patterns mak.
A clanjamfrie o verses rife
wie rhymes that wi maun tak
thinkin tae bield wir ain sells
wie warkit wuid an healin herb
no spierin whit the lift tells
o growin sair an twistit verb.
The makar's gift comes nae alane:
the cleared wuid; the fellin pain.

8   Fermers ken the wie hame
the fisherman sees the seas
huntin the weit forests, same
wie the kep an nae sudden freeze
but catcht live an eaten then:
warm bluid the taste maks
teeth puu throbbin flesh
sinews spat oot ae mooth taks
the rare muscle fresh;
clans share the kill they ken.
In derk wuids the tools are born.

hairy haunds the tannel form,
intae wide plains they are torn
noo tae ken the muckle harns storm
whaur the strecht backs brocht ben.
Oan twae feet the hunter bides
the pattern sties the same
the kep, the kill frae awe sides
the chaunce is aye tae blame;
the hunteds daunce says when.

14 Warkin the wuid thegither
wing wild hingin tae brainches
sherp taes wark wi feather
the balance o fuid tae fund.
Noo wie shift wi the yirds wund
takin the paitern o stick staund
ain sang the haill sang wrenches
the clan shifts as a band
a blinterin blae o a saund shift
washed oan the shores o the lift
The virr an smeddum o lika grain
wi licht the yird drenches
a keekin gless o fine saft rain
blinterin doon amin bare brainches
warkan the wuid takan wir chaunces.

Harvey Holton

Frae the Chinese o Qiao Jifu

Pairtin

i   "The Phoenix Seeks its Marra"
        hairpin on a slaw air
    "The Oreole Seeks its Maik" –
        dinna sing yon sang.
    the Deas of the Sun's cuttit aff aathegither
        frae the Lether ti the Cairrie
    an Peach Flouer Glen's awa
        whaur Wastlin Roads is Dour.

ii   nae en ti't, nae shore
    sair hairt-scauds
        like a bleck sea
    sorra thraws ma wame
        in thousans o knots

doublt tears
   in ma ill-daein een
tears i the een
   sorra i the wame
the deein flame
   dwynin incense
     still ti thole
i the wee hours
   waitin on ma luve
(she'll shuirlie come
   inti ma dream?)
hou'll A can staun
   the cauld cod
     the wearie covers?

iii   fouterin wi her dulcimer
derk flauchts o hair letten doun
never eident wi her luiks, A mind
luve's langsyne turnt her ti idleset
naither kaimed nor made up
bonnie ti see,
   her naitral sel.

iv   bells on the wind
   A think on bracelets
sauchtrees bent i the haar
   is't her froun?
her ivorie kaim
   the new mune's horn
her brou A mind
   a lillie-flouer
the peachtree's flourish
   och, it's like her face

weimen o the east
   southron lassies
they're braw aneuch ti see
but their ivorie clappers
   their siller dulcimers
     they've scunnert me.

v   A'm gyte gane wi luve
   whan'll A be easy in masel?
mairatowre
A'm feelin that forhooiet
   naither bite nor sup A pree
it's aa ti thole –
   the seas gaun dry
   rocks meltin wi the sun

Checkin masel

sittin idle i the caller airs
sleepin hie mang cluds o white
nae leivin sowl gobs in ma gub
A'll stot-stot wi pleisur
an lauch – haw-haw

see ither fowk
   yokit an shoved about
   worn doun ti the back-hauf
aa ti mak a cannie wee bield

east?
   it's up ti me
wast?
   it's up ti me.

Greinin for luve

ablow a pale mune
peirtrees wind
   inlang the palins
     bend aside them
caller dew on blae moss
   weit
     cauld on stockins o gauze
missin him
   ma hairt braks for sorra

up the haill nicht
   burnin incense
     for the sake o him

Speakin o masel

A never ettlt ti be the Dux
wis never in the Buik o Warthie Men
Sanct o the Dram
   onie time
Precentor o Poetry
   onie whaur
Tap o the Cless
   for rouks an dawin cluds
Drucken Immortal
   o watter an lochside

for bletherin an lauchin
A sud be
    Compiler ti the Faculty

hingin about for fortie year
   o scrievin the wind
   an dichtin the mune

At Thornieburn

A speir at the houses
   on Thornieburn side
whae's aucht them?
nae ploums plantit
auld trees haudin up the yetts
wild rashes taiglin the bankins
withert bamboo smoorin the palins
an abbey wi nae freirs
   sclaits rummelt wi the tods
a court wi nae pleas
   bleck rottans for the gairds
white watter
   yalla sand

A've leaned owre aa the railins
an ilka skreichin corbie's
   been
      countit.

Ma Zhiyuan

I the haar, the abbey's gloamin bell

cauld haar thins
   the auld abbey comes clear
oncome o the derknin
   worshippers gie owre
     are still

thrie-fower times on a wastlin wund
   the jow o the evenin bell
wad this mak an auld monk
   set ti his meditation?

Owreset bi Brian Holton

Sandie Craigie

Bi-lingual

I speak in Scots, write in English
I speak in Scots, write in English
I speak in Scots, write in English
I speak in slang, write in English
I ought not to write with a Scottish accent
I write in English, write in English
Think in Scots, translate... translate...
How does NOT mean why
How does NOT mean why
Pronounce OU not OO
House, mouse, now, tousey – WRONG
Ja – louse – WRONG
Jalouse – Wrong
Think "jalouse" – say "guess"
Think in Scots with an English accent
Resist... resist...
I fight in Scots, I must NOT fight
discuss in English
I must pass in the English language
Pass – fail – resist
Think – don't think – think
I scream in Scots
I am Scots – with an English accent
I am English – with a Scots accent
Must not be proud
must not be loud
bite this tongue
and it hurts
and sometimes

I bleed in Scots
Dream in colour
Write in black and white
...weep in Scots.

Visiting

The starched sheets are cold
and give you rashes you say,
then turn to stare out the Autumn window.
It's visiting time
and silence drapes itself between us
adding friction to each slow second.

Awkward, I shuffle
and force each tense muscle
into a weak smile.
After a while you turn to me
your eyes have caught the mottled glass
of the window.

You try to talk
Through oxygen mask and tears
you muffle and sqawk your apology
And only Christ,
if he exists here
knows why I resist the words
grit them between my teeth

The bell rings
bringing relief, drowned
by the clash of stacking chairs
and fast feet.
I walk, tearswept
the length of the ward
stopping for a last look

My eyes paint the scene
Watercolour
Still life.

Woman

She is the wind and the sun
the blue that bleeds red
the wordless poet
the voiceless song
the crucifix... and the bed.
Inside her head, a hundred doves
The Ravens pray
behind
a mask of many faces
She sees
yet in her vision... blind
She has known love
yet in her inconsistency... alone
She is the still loch
the cornered sea
Timeless, yet in time
a wife... mother... lover
She is the child that life forgot
She is the Christ in me.

Hame comin

Queer, an a' these familiar
unfamiliar buildings. Staines oan stanes
wee-er an mair gray
than ma mind can mind ae
Nameless faimlies' washin
hung oot, dreepin buntin
fir this grand hame-comin

An the cheers ir seagulls
greetin, coorsin skyless
fleein tenement-weys
It's a' the life aboon
an nane tae see it

Strange, yit stranger still
the wind-snarled coarners
gairdin gleemin windaes that
dreep thir white lids lady-like
tae hide thir eyes
An whaur's the time when
honest windaes wid be flung wide
fir a' tae see. Noo prideless
they gawk in privacy

An passin yince kent backgreens
noo ca'd yairds. Wi flooers
an gress wi edges
an haurd crooned railins
wi creakless gates ye cannae swing oan
an widnae want tae

Hear, somewhaur a boanfire's embers
whisper tae me
Nae place left, nae place at a'
Still ma voice spills in empty tenements
that nane remembers.

SCOTS LANGUAGE RESOURCE CENTRE

The Scots Language Resource Centre his been foundit i the Sandeman Library in Perth tae gie us a national centre fir the Scots leid. The Centre is tae be a library o aakin material, texts, tapes etc in oor national leid, an a central information storage an referral point fir informatioun aboot ilka level o activity relatit tae the mither tongue.

Stertin frae an initiative bi the Scots Language Society an supportit bi a haill swathe o academic, educational an sic like institutions, frae next yeir the Centre'll be housit i the new Perth library bein biggit i York Place. Fundin fir the Centre an a wheen o major projects is bein sought frae government, commerce an industry, trust funds an ony fowk wi siller tae spare. Gif ye want tae ken whit's whit, we're the fowk tae ask.

Mair details frae Stuart McHardy, Director SLRC, The Sandeman Library, 16 Kinnoull St, Perth PH1 5ET or gie us a bell on our 0738 440199 at ony time – we hae an ansafone – awfy hi-tech!

SLRC Association Membership

Subscribers: £15   Concessions (OAP, UB40): £5
Institutions: £40   Corporate members £100
Varorium, oor quarterly members' newsletter/journal wull bring thegither aa the multifarious Scots language activities an interests o the present day.

The Fower Fiers

Sheena Blackhall

Fionn o the Knoc, haein gaithered saxty years at his back, wi neither wife nur bairn tae caa his ain, an nae kin leevin ava, wad takk tae hissel fower fiers frae the breets o the air. Frae the lea o Craig nam Ban, far the pines are a green plaidie, far in auldlangsyne the North fowk burned their witches, he wyled Darroch the ern, fa's virr is weel-kent in the heich places. Frae the watters o Loch Davan, far the Pict chiels plytered an fished in the langdeidtimes, he wyled Deirdre the swan, fa's bonnieness is brichter nur the meen: Deirdre the swan fa's beauty reisted the verra pike that coories amang the seggs. Fae the braes o Beinn a Bhuird, far the win blaws keen's an arra an it's a fack weel-kent that the warrior Feinn are sleepin, he wyled Coinneach the Craw, fa is sleekit an fly. Hinmaist, frae a whin buss in the parks o Aucholzie back o Lochnagar, fraw the park o the bard's coo (in the auld spikk o the Gaels fa aince bedd there), he wyled Kirsty the jenny wren, fa's wird is sweet an cantie, fa's een are twa blaeberries, fa cud sattle snod in a bairn's neive, an yon neive steekit.

Fower winged fiers he tuik tae bide wi him, did Fionn o the Knoc, till he micht chuse fit ain tae keep foriver an ay. An ilkie fier hid a vertue, aa its ain... Darroch the ern wi his braid, braid showders wis strang an powerfu; Daedalus hissel micht hae biggit him. Deirdre the swan's grait vertue wis bonnieness; sic grace gleddened the sicht. She wis a true bairn o Leda, fite an soople, swippert an swack's a kelpie. Coinneach the craw, wis wyled bi Fionn fur his thrift, a guid Scots vertue in a puir kintra. naethin wis wastit fin Coinneach wis tae the fore. Ain o Gandhi's untouchables, the warld wad rikk wi the scunnersome guff o orrals wioot his powkin neb. Hinmaist ava bobbit Kirsty the wee jenny wren, an her grait vertue wis music. Faith, Orpheus wad hae follaed her frae Hades itsel, an nae dour-faced neither, fur the teenie bird hid blytheness, as well as rhythm, strung tae the clarsach o her thrapple.

They war the fower fiers Fionn o the Knoc tuik tae bide wi him, till he micht chuse fit ain tae keep. Fur anely a gype poors wine inoo a yird quaich, an Fionn wis sikkin an heir tae owergie the hairst o his years, his wyes an his wyceness, the heirship o his kennin, an the kennin o his deid clann's afore him. Sic kennin wad bi spyled in the lug an hairt o a gowk.

Noo they warna lang sattled thegither fin Fionn o the Knoc hid a dwaum, that the boolie o stanes he caad hame maun be dinged doon tae the girse. An he jaloused it wis time tae rigg fur the road, the thin fite road that twines frae the Knoc ben the howes an knowes o the north. An aince on the road, ilkie fier wad be pit tae the test, tae see gin its mettle wis richt an fittin tae cairry the heirskip o Fionn of the Knoc's deid clann. At cock-craw neist mornin, the auld bodach smoored the fire wi aisse, dang a stick throw the reef-thatch an dinged doon the waas o his steadin wide tae the fower wins, settin aff ower the thin fite road wi ainely a daud o bried an

a suppie cheese rowed up in a cloot tae ett, wi the fower fiers flichterin roon him.

On his richt haun wis Darroch the ern, raxxin his muckle wings. Darroch the ern, Fionn prized for his virr. An the muckle bird wis sib tae Fionn in a fey wye, bi rizzen o his thrawnness, fur Fionn wis sweir tae shift frae a notion fin aince he'd taen it, an Darroch wad niver devaul frae catchin a prey.

Farrer ower, flew Coinneach the craw, cryin ta-ta tae the Knoc an the craiturs that bide aboot the cornparks an dykes, Coinneach, fa Fionn prized fur his thrift, fa wis sib tae Fionn in a fey wye, bi rizzen o his cannie natur. Fur Coinneach wadna set neb tae maet, afore takkin tent that nae tribble wis wytin tae gar him claw far he wisna yoky… as Fionn wadna steer wioot raxxin his harns an takkin maitters weel throw haun.

The swack an gracefu Deirdre glided ahin, Deirdre frae the shores o Loch Davan, prized bi Fionn fur her bonnieness. An the fite, fite swan wis sib tae Fionn in a fey wye, bi rizzen o her grace, fur the weeminfowk o his clann war aa gran dauncers, fleet fittit, wi the reels an hoolichans o the Gael bred inno them aa.

Hinmaist ava bobbit Kirsty the jenny wren, fa Fionn prized fur her music… the wye she tweetled the notes sae lichtsome, gaed kittlesome roon his hairt like a hairy wirm. An wee Kirsty wren wis sib tae Fionn anna in a fey wye, fur he'd bin a dab haun at the pibroch fin his hauns war younger.

They'd traivelled a fair puckle miles fin they cam tae the Futterat's Brig, that rowed its back like a spittin stoat abune the burn, the brig that wis nerra an roch wi Spring's fite thaws, an Winter's blaik-hairted haars. Haudin the croon o the brig wis a cocky young fawn, fa wad neither shift nur shoo.

"Haud ower, haud ower, frien fawn", quo Fionn kindly.

"Cam forrit or back that we micht cross the brig."

Bit the young fawn cockit its heid sidiewyes, an coost its spinnle shanks ootower fur coorseness an wadna flit nur flee.

"I haud ower fur naebody, auld bodach", quo the bigsie fawn. "Ma faither is Euan the stag, the laird o saxteen hinds, the faither o hunners o deer fowk. I willna shift nur shoo." Syne, Darroch the ern, fa's virr is weel kent in the heich places, climmed tae a grait cloud, dauchled a wee, an drappt like a steen on the back o the bigsie fawn, heistin it up in his clooks ootower a cliff an a corrie, awa frae Fionn's sicht. Efter a wee, the muckle bird flew back. His clooks war reid's a rose, an spirks o crammosie glimmered alang his neb.

Wae, syne, wis the hairt of Fionn o the Knoc, fur he kent that virr is nae a vertue, lessen it mells wi mercie.

"Gyang hame, gyang hame tae the lea o Craig nam Ban far the pines are a green plaidie", he cried tae Darroch the ern. "Ye's be ower fierce, ower fierce tae traivel the road wi me." At yon, the grait bird raisse up inno the lift like a cross, wi Fionn's hairt preened tilt, fur he'd lued the bird like his ain bairn.

Ower the brig gaed the lave, an foremaist ava gaed Deirdre the swan, like a queen, fa's bonnieness wis brichter nur the meen. On an on alang the thin fite foad they daundered, till they stoppit at a widlan puil, a blaik, blaik puil aneth a dowie, derksome fir. An frae its midnicht deeps there lowped a taed, an ill-faird warty taed, the keeper o the widlan puil fa stude afore them.

"Haud ower, haud ower frien taed", quo Fionn o the Knoc. "Either gyang back or cam forrit, fur we hae a pouerfu drooth an fain wad weet wir thrapples."

Noo the taed lowpit aside, fur it wis a couthie craitur, bit Deirdre the swan frae the watters o Loch Davan, far the muckle pike dwaums in the seggs, Deirdre the swan, fa's bonnieness is brichter than the meen, hissed an hubbered an hissed in a cauld fizz. "Dae ye think I'd sup frae a puil that a scunnersome taed his fyled?" she speired. "Sic an orra, fyachy, gyad-sake tink o a taed as yon?" An she booed her thrapple sideiwise, like an aidder, raxxin tae strikk.

Afore Fionn o the Knoc cud spikk, the taed's een glimmered, an the midnicht deeps o the puil turned cauld as ice.

"Tho ye willna sup bonnie birdie, ye may surely luik", quo the keeper o the widlan puil. An the bonnie, vauntie swan glowered lang an lang at her ainsel in the blaik, blaik watter, fair transmogrified.

"Bide or gyang, bide or gyang", quo the taed tae Fionn o the Knoc. "She willna hear ye. The gowk is catched bi her ain pride, a prisoner o the widlan puil foriver an ay." Dowie-hairted, Fionn o the Knoc agreed, fur fin bonnieness mells wi pride it losses aa enchantment.

Smaa in nummer noo gaed the lave o the fiers, bi the derk an dowie fir, alang the neuks an twines o the thin fite road, till the sun stuid heich i the lift like a fechter's targ, a targ that wis burnished gowd. Hungert an trauchelt, trauchelt an hungert, they dowpit doon aneth a birk, an Fionn o the Knock tuik oot his pyock o breid an cheese, an pairtit it oot, a daud fur hissel, a bittick fur Coinneach the craw, an a nippick fur Kirsty, the wee jenny wren.

Nae suner hid he dane't, than Coinneach the craw frae the braes o Beinn a Bhuird, far the wins blaw keen's an arra, reived the nippick o maet frae the teeny-weeny birdie an gollupt it doon in a trice.

Syne wae wis the hairt o Fionn o the Knoc, fur fin thrift mells wi avarice, it bladds ony vertue ava, as dubs fyle a bonnie, glintin puil.

"Gyang hame, gyang hame, Coinneach the craw", quo Fionn in an angeret vyce. "Ye are gutsy an sleekit, sleekit an gutsy. I willna share ma wyes an ma wyceness, an the kennin o ma clann, wi ye."

Sae Coinneach the craw flappit oot ower the dyke like an auld cloot in the win, hyne aff tae his cauld hame, and Fionn o the Knock stude alane, wi Kirsty the jenny wren, fa gleddened the day wi her wheeplin an lichtsome ploys.

"Ah," thocht the old bodach, "jimp an sma, jimp an sma, the jenny wren's the best ava. She shall be ma flier, tae share the hairst o my years, my wyes an wyceness wi."

Bit noo, the twa stude fair at the jynin o three roads, an Fionn stoppit a wee, fur he wis weariet an trauchlet. He cockit a thochtfu ee tae ilkie airt. Tae the North, the thin fite road raxxed up tae a misty ben, bare's a bane, teetin heich tae the meen, wi steens as fite's a skull on ilkie side. An yon wis the road o the warlock, the priest, the seer, the secund sichted, an the spay-wife, fa's trade is dwaums an signs an omens, fur dwaums alane cud saften yon lanely braes that yawned like a wolf's mawe tae the starns abune. Mony's the ain fa gaed yon verra gait, the bard, the artist, the piper, traivelled ower near tae the cliff side, an drapt tae the enless pit-murk Hell o the clean-wud. Tae the east ran a sanny road, that ran bi a sweet wee burn, far oot tae a green horizon. Corn an girse, bird an breet delichtit tae gyang yon gait, far fowk war far an fyew, an fairm, an nest, an tod's, derk, den, bedd thegither in girse an tree an knowe. Yon wis the road o pleuman, gangrel, tink, an the antrin quate fisher, far ilkie chiel keeps his ain coonsel, an bothers nane.

Tae the wast wis a steery road, that lowpt frae toun tae toun, far girse wis fenced an tramplit, bladded an filed, far the lift wis blaik wi the rikk o a thoosan factories, far fowk trauchled like ants in their ain dirt, an the verra rain wis traikit wi glaur. Frae yon three, Fionn maun chuse. Wi a licht hairt he pykit the sanny road, the road his ain deid clann wad hae pykit, that ran bi a sweet caller burnie oot tae the green horizon, far the leddylanders bide, an the wattergaw hides its fairy crock o gowd. The teeny Kirsty the wren, anely dauchled on the wing a hair's breadth efter yon. Twa, three secunds she swithered, syne breenged tae the wast, cairryin her sang tae the cassies o a stoory toun.

"Come back, come back" cried Fionn o the Knoc tae the teenie birdie. "I hae muckle tae teach ye, muckle tae teach ye, an muckle tae gie, muckle tae gie."

"An sae hae I", quo the wee, wee bird. "There's fowk in the toun wad be gled o a wee jenny wren, fur her ainsel. I hae ma ain sangs tae gie, ma ain wyes, an ma ain wyceness. The weird I dree shall niver mell wi yers."

An Kirsty the jenny wren left the auld bodach at the crossin o the fower roads, fur her road wis jist stertin, an Fionn's wis near dane. An poorin oot the bonnie sang frae her thrapple, she bobbit awa tae the touns far the wast wis wytin.

Sheena Blackhall

The John Macmurray Centenary

Stanley M Harrison

On October 17 1991, the centenary of John Macmurray's birth was honoured with a three-day gathering/conference at Marquette University, Milwaukee, Wisconsin, *God, Earth and Human Community: the Post-Modern Religious Philosophy of John Macmurray*. Two dozen papers had been submitted to the committee. Participants were drawn from Australia, England, Belgium, Scotland, and by the opening dinner, nearly fifty persons assembled in Milwaukee to celebrate and cultivate the influential thought of this remarkable philosopher. One most gratifying aspect of the event was hearing from so many people, including non-academics, delighted to learn of the existence of a Macmurray Society.

The John Macmurray Society was initiated *c.*1970 through the efforts of Reginald Sayers of Toronto, who had begun a correspondence with John Macmurray and put much labour into bringing together interested persons in and around Toronto to discuss his work. He also published a newsletter and started a collection of Macmurray's writings, books and out-of-print pamphlets, which he made available at nominal cost. Virtually single-handed, he sustained a Macmurray Society for several years. After his death in the late 1970s it existed in name only until in 1989 Frank Kirkpatrick wrote to a number of people suggesting a meeting at Trinity University in Hartford, Connecticut, where he is Professor of Religion. To his surprise, fifteen of us made the trip. Thus began the resurgence of the International John F. Macmurray Society, and discussion began on the possibility of a centenary conference. In 1990 the society met in June at Marquette, where papers were read and discussed by about twenty participants. Thanks to significant subsidies from Marquette University there could be wide advertising, and it was possible to invite speakers. The 1991 centenary meeting was the first fully formed conference of the Macmurray society, and marks, it is hoped, a watershed for the future.

The people who came to Marquette were excited to be together to honour Macmurray and to discuss and interpret what all see as the importance of his original work. In his welcoming remarks at the opening dinner the programme committee chair spoke to the remarkable fact that it was the spirit of fidelity to Macmurray and his work which had brought the participants from great distances together to work co-operatively toward realising what Macmurray called 'the personal life'. The range of presentations at the various sessions clearly reflected the wide relevance of his seminal and provocative ideas.

The first paper, by A.R.C.Duncan, sounded the challenge which often perplexes those who are familiar with Macmurray. 'John Macmurray: A Neglected Philosopher' spoke to fundamental themes of importance still inadequately recognised by the larger academic world. This paper effectively reminded everyone of the Macmurray Society's basic agenda:

to continue to bring John Macmurray to the attention of thoughtful persons everywhere.

On Friday, papers in both general and concurrent sessions explored various motifs focussed primarily on issues to do with the way Macmurray understood agency; the quest for objectivity; the novelty and importance of his views of rationality, particularly emotional rationality. Professor Frances Berenson, of the University of London, challenged the audience with what she saw as certain inadequacies of Macmurray's understanding of personal and impersonal relations. Several took up her challenge and politely served up criticisms of her heavily analytic treatment. Later in the morning there was a chance to hear how both radical subjectivists and deconstructionists could learn from Macmurray's nuanced discussions of the ways in which objectivity is to be understood. Another paper showed how close Macmurray and Plato really are on the oft-misunderstood reason vs. emotion issue.

Macmurray's insights into emotional rationality (and their pedagogical implications) were provocatively explored by Professor Thomas Owens of Rhode Island, in his paper 'The Vocation of the Artist'. Professor Ghislain Florival of Louvain, Belgium, spoke about the understanding of the affectivity of persons in Macmurray's *Persons in Relation*. Her own perspective is informed by training in phenomenology and a long interest in Freud's reflections on the character of the interpersonal. One challenge she raised was whether Macmurray accurately understood the dynamics of sexual relations. Audience members less sympathetic to Freud were not persuaded that Macmurray was naïve about the mother-child relation. Other papers pursued dimensions of Macmurray's phenomenological analysis of persons. Giving another indication of the diverse influence of Macmurray, Robert Daly MD, Professor of Psychiatry at the State University of New York at Syracuse, intrigued many with his discussion of Macmurray's importance for understanding 'The Problem of Madness'.

The evening's dinner was graced by the personal reminiscences of several who had known Macmurray personally and/or corresponded with him. Afterwards Peter Walton from Australia and Philip Hunt from the UK – friends for many decades – spoke of first making acquaintance with Macmurray's writings in the 1930s. Others regaled us with anecdotes and personal impressions of Macmurray and his artist wife Betty. The Quaker educationist Kenneth Barnes, who has known Macmurray since the early 1930s and written of his ideas in several books, had taken great trouble to record memories on tape, having regretfully relinquishing hope of attending in person. This was heard with much appreciation.

On Saturday morning, Frank Kirkpatrick spoke in a session on 'The Logic of Heterocentrism: Receiving the Self as Gift'. Later papers directed attention to Macmurray's reflections on 'friendship', linking him with figures such as Aristotle and Aquinas; others pursued political themes in Macmurray, searching out his relevance for understanding the difficult connections between religion, democracy and the contemporary search for community.

Later, Philip Mooney spoke of Macmurray's critiques of the Church and offered new insights regarding Macmurray's scepticism about institutionalised religion, and how Macmurray understood integrity as the centre of one's personal life. His confrontations with the dangers of dogma in religion were juxtaposed nicely with his recognition that many of his kindred spirits among professional academics were American Jesuits who responded warmly and enthusiastically to his work on the nature of persons and his defence of theism.

The relevance of Macmurray for contemporary developments in the world was the central theme of the closing general session. In 'John Macmurray and Contextual Theology' Christopher Lind of St Andrew's College, Saskatoon, gave a talk devoted to the importance of Macmurray as a resource for thinking about issues in 'liberation' theology. By the time the discussion ended, one could not but be impressed with how deeply and richly Macmurray's ideas have taken hold in so many areas of contemporary thinking, not only among academics but with people involved in counselling, pastoral work, hospital administration, criminal justice systems, *et al*. As was proved in the 1930s when he gave a series of talks on the BBC (later published as *Freedom in the Modern World*) and stirred audiences throughout Britain, Macmurray continues to reach non-academics through the clarity of his writings and the depth of his insights.

Stanley M. Harrison

In part due to the persuasiveness of Fr. John Costello SJ, President of Regis College, Toronto, by the date of the centenary Humanities Press had agreed to reissue in North American paperback editions *The Self as Agent, Persons in Relation, Freedom in the Modern World* and *Reason and Emotion*. Since then, *The Conditions of Freedom* and *Interpreting the Universe* also have appeared. Each edition has a new introduction. Father Costello also reminded people that the collection of Macmurray materials originally garnered by Reggie Sayers, both primary and secondary sources, continues to grow, available to researchers at the Regis College Library. There is a large archive at Edinburgh University.

Six out of some two dozen conference papers was published in the journal *Philosophy and Theology*, Vol 6 No 4, Summer 1992 (Marquette University Press): those above-noted by Ewens, Mooney, Lind, Kirkpatrick, Cizewski and Florival. Copies are available in paper and on disk. Inquiries to Stanley Harrison, Dept. of Philosophy, Marquette University, Milwaukee, Wisconsin, USA 53233. First in a proposed series of books devoted to Macmurray, A.R.C. Duncan's *The Nature of Persons* is a clear, thorough exposition (Peter Lang, Bern, £25). Beside Jeanne Warren's *Becoming Real* (Ebor Press) another pamphlet, *John Macmurray in a Nutshell* (Handsel Press, Edinburgh, £2.95) has a useful bibliography to set beside that in the Festschrift, *The Personal Universe*, ed. Thos. Wren (Humanities Press, 1975). Another book of essays by contemporary scholars on or influenced by Macmurray, is in preparation, ed. Harry Carson. Other books are Frank Kirkpatrick's *Community: A Trinity of Approaches*, which puts Macmurray's understanding of the person in relation to the thought of liberal political philosophers (Rawls, Locke, Hobbes &c.) as well as Marx; and in philosophy Whitehead &c.

Scheduled for October 9–12, 1993 at Fitchburg State College, Fitchburg, Massachusetts, the next meeting of the International Macmurray Society takes for its theme: *Society in Transition: The Macmurrayan Vision of the Social/Cultural Transformation of Modern Life*. Inquiries to Professor Peter Cordella, South Hall, Saint Anselm College, Manchester, New Hampshire, USA 03102.

Macmurray – Man and Mind

Robert Calder

Macmurray's first book, *Freedom in the Modern World*, grew from a series of radio talks given on the BBC in 1932. Producer C.A. Siepmann wrote of the 1932 broadcasts:

> Few would have expected that ... twelve broadcast talks on Philosophy would have produced a miniature renaissance, among thousands of ... listeners. ...What was impressive about these broadcast talks was the emotional intensity of the response to a new challenge to self-examination ... they speak a language undistorted by false associations.

Through the following decades Macmurray continued to write books and deliver talks addressed to an intelligent and questioning general public. With British academic philosophy turning into a specialist technical study, he did not regard himself as a populariser. He saw his work as representing a different development, more in keeping with philosophy's past, and relevant to modern problems. He believed it should engage with, and improve the standard of, public debate about official policy. Macmurray asked questions about the boundaries between government and non-intervention; spoke and wrote about art, religion, psychology, education, motivation and intention.

He was born in Kirkcudbright in 1891, went to school in Aberdeen and, while a student at Glasgow University and at Oxford, pondered various possible careers. War interrupted his studies – he had crucial experiences confronting death and, after being badly wounded and brought home, public hostility toward an unknown enemy. That he became a university teacher of philosophy – with professorships at London (1928–44) and Edinburgh (1944–58) – was no matter of following a special aptitude, he insists in his brief autobiography *Search for Reality in Religion*. His nephew Duncan Campbell was recently amazed by the huge extent of Macmurray's extra-mural work in the 1930s, talking, attending discussions of public issues. There was even a visit to Spain during the civil war,

> with a group of people who were anxious to see for themselves ... I with ... others went to the Basque country and were guests of the Basque government in Bilbao. While there we saw the first bombardment of a town by an air force ...(by Italian and German planes mainly). ... I wrote the report of the whole group, and sent it to *The Times*. No reply...

Macmurray refused to join a 1937 deputation to Nazi Germany because the Nazis' willingness to 'discuss' was not a mark of reasonableness but implied British toleration of the undiscussed persecution of the Jews.

He became involved, too, with the British Council on its foundation in 1945, and a talk given under their auspices during a visit to Rome in 1950 sheds light on another of his interests, the Adult Education College at Newbattle Abbey:

> The major difficulty was money – in particular, could the college be made to pay its way; if so, how; and if it failed to do this who would guarantee the deficit? ...When I joined the Newbattle Abbey College Committee I took a

strong line in recommending the reopening of the college as a full time adult education college ... With her great tradition of educational passion and creation, she is capable of the best and deserves the best. Let's take our courage in both hands and set it going. The money will surely be found somehow.

Edwin Muir was appointed to preside pending closure of a moribund institute, but his imagination and organising ability worked wonders. The man who came out from London to close up found it thriving. As a friend, Macmurray knew Muir's talents: they had co-operated during the war, and Macmurray wanted to create "the kind of college for which Edwin was an ideal head", as he notes in letters to Muir's widow.

> I had no interest in making Newbattle pay its way by lowering its ideas of adult education. I wanted the kind of college that Edwin was running, I had no desire or sympathy for anything else. I thought that, given time, it could be maintained: and I was involved, more directly, in building up the extramural department of the University in the South-East, and was being successful. The year after I retired the University Adult Education Department enrolled over 5,000 students in Edinburgh and the South-East of Scotland. I had hoped that this could eventually be the feeder for Newbattle students. ... it became clear to me that I was standing alone, and that alas! Scotland was no longer interested in education even to the extent that England was ...

"It was," Macmurray writes, "a struggle of public policy over the kind of college that Scotland needed and was prepared to support", and when all his hopes were done Macmurray hung on as Governor only until Muir was invited to lecture at Harvard. During this period Macmurray prepared and delivered his Gifford Lectures, tried out at his friend George Macleod's Iona, and was also having difficulties with his university department:

> I set myself to hold the fort for Edwin, and when the invitation to Harvard came to him I heaved a great sigh of relief and decided that as soon as the occasion arose, after Edwin was gone I should resign. I was free, I felt, to shake the dust of Newbattle off my feet...

He was still, during these years, Professor of Moral Philosophy at Edinburgh. Arnold Kemp, editor of *The Herald*, has paid considerable tribute to Macmurray's lively teaching. The poets Tessa Ransford and Tom Scott also speak of those lectures, the latter of "a kindly, white-haired man, who always waited at the end for any questions any of the large class might wish to come up to him with". In a 1988 talk to Edinburgh Arts Club Tessa Ransford recalled a poetry-reading on a tour of Canada, after which she was startled to be asked if she had read Macmurray. When she said she had attended his lectures she was invited to speak of him to a philosophy class, and was amazed at how much she could recall, from the extent to which the different elements of her M.A. course had seemed each to combine into meaning, to an impression common to many that somehow Macmurray's teaching had become integral to her individual life. In Macmurray's books, she noted,

> the arguments are clear and set out in plain language without jargon, as were his lectures, which were so popular that students (and staff!) from all faculties crowded in to hear them and sets of notes were pounced on avidly by those who couldn't make their own.

Macmurray's audience at times numbered four hundred, and the venue of his lectures had to be changed. Mimeograph copies survive of at least one

John Macmurray photographed in 1936

session's lectures, taken down in shorthand. Like other legendary Scottish Moral Philosophy Professors recalled by non-philosopher students, Macmurray doubtless owes some fame to a personal moral impressiveness and a spoken delivery aware of his audience as well as what was to be communicated. Like Francis Hutcheson at Glasgow in the eighteenth century, Macmurray has been wrongly supposed rather the preacher than anything else, for he spoke earnestly with involvement. As the mimeograph shows, these lectures were not short on content. Addressed to mostly younger members of the public, rather than academics, their effect on sometime students – teachers, artists, journalists, legislators, administrators – is perhaps history. Differently arranged, their substance is happily also in his books.

The North American universities' initial debt to Hutcheson's Scotland has lately been repaid in writings about it by alumni studying it as their own culture. Equally, whereas Macmurray is known to few Scots his writings would interest, he has been considerably championed, his books reprinted, in North America, where his centenary was well celebrated.

Britain now has in 'The John Macmurray Fellowship' a modest venture to help restore his work to attention. Unhappily recent nationalistic claims that Macmurray characteristically represents a marginalised Scottish culture, victim of anglicisation, were attended by extensive misreading of his thought. Tom Scott recalls, from Macmurray's account of the Hebraic legacy to Europe of the west, reference to a prophetic function such as, for instance, Marx exercised by the writing of books: not necessarily by affirming a creed, rather by restoring attention to reality. This was Macmurray's task and function.

Prolegomena to Macmurray's Philosophy

At the time of John Macmurray's birth, there were a dozen or so philosophy teachers in Scottish universities, hardly more in English ones. While a specialist publication called *Mind* had run some fifteen years, there was no specialist readership in any number. Its public had been much the same as read articles on philosophy beside translations from Pushkin *et cetera* in such journals as *Blackwood's* and *Edinburgh Review*. The philosophical writing was however of a high standard, and the themes are hardly dated. There was even one critique of the historically important Scottish philosopher Sir William Hamilton (d.1856).

Hamilton had rejected a prevailing argumentative theology; striving to make room for a genuine spirituality he advanced the notion that reality is an object only of faith or intuition, and is strictly unknowable. The relation to Macmurray is plain, given Hamilton's dependence on the German 'faith philosophy' of Hamann and Jacobi. At the beginning of Macmurray's 1950s Gifford Lectures, in *The Self as Agent*, there is a critique of that 'faith philosophy'. When Robert Flint wrote a comprehensive analysis in his book *Agnosticism* (1902), this addressed both Hamilton's attempted defence of spirituality, and other theories of an unknowable whose intent was to deny all cognitive reality to moral experience, and treat everything as physico-chemical processes of which there is no consciousness. By the time of *The Self as Agent* Macmurray had the further resource of being able to cite the Nazi doctrine of blood-intuition of an otherwise inaccessible ultimate reality. The notion that truth is found by 'feeling' is dangerously formulated in English, that has also been confused with emotional intensity: I *feel* it. As Macmurray notes in a book strongly critical of the *Reason and Emotion* dualism, a feeling regardless of intensity can be wrong, and is *no* warrant of sureness.

Any notion of Macmurray rising up on behalf of what might be called 'Free will, Individuality, the Soul &c' in the face of a 20th century onslaught, has to be ditched. In his own penetrating analysis, such an automatic mischaracterisation is the product of two not separate but distinguishable habits of mind, dualist and aestheticist. In Macmurray's analysis one aspect of the 'aesthetic' is its final recourse to what people can agree about together. People can agree with each other that they will disagree on some questions, that viewpoints or religious/cultural beliefs seem impossible to reconcile, and further have agreed to the statement that there is no objective truth. As Plato however points out, that statement lays claim to objective truth. For Macmurray, philosophy cannot consistently pretend to any truth without acknowledging that there is objective truth, and actually seeking that truth rather than seeking to agree for the sake of agreement – or to disagree in the cause of some supposed refinement of discourse.

Facts are not facts because they are agreed. Macmurray has more to say about the denial of objectivity. Behind it lies a confrontation with German materialist doctrine of the 19th century, from which, as the Edinburgh philosopher Andrew Seth noted, Nietzsche collected a lot of tags continued in currency by his writings.

In claiming that Macmurray has things to say today, it is useful to note how far he was continuing earlier debates. In *The Boundaries of Science* (1938, with Hitler on the horizon) Macmurray contrasts a *theological* account of free will with a doctrine of Unconsciousness which, pressed to consistency, does *not* regard 'mind' as just so many physico-chemical processes. Theories of physics and chemistry are in that analysis indistinguishable from fairy stories. One of the curiosities, as Macmurray sees, is that some people have tried to draw conclusions from this sort of view, launching in the 19th century a quest for 'absolute certainty'. Macmurray certainly believed that the extreme view of the unknowability of reality was irrefutable, that there is no answer to it, but that it can have absolutely no implications. He remained permanently aware that to try to deal with any such theory along with, say, scientific discourse or even casual conversation, is at once to concede and to deny that one is talking nonsense. If true, neither the hypothesis nor anything else matters. It can enter thought only as an aesthetic notion, and can't even imply loving one another or strict moral rectitude as a bulwark against its supposed truth.

In his 1928 lecture 'The Unity of Modern Problems', Macmurray makes it plain that he is against compartmentalisation, and, equally that he understands problems of apperception such as Georg Simmel raised in his 'Man and Woman'. Logical translation of the denial of objectivity produces of course (a) I want to avoid thinking about things, (b) I want however to pretend that I *have* thought fully about things.

Macmurray's account of the aesthetic fallacy further points to the character of confused individualism. This is obviously enough the *argumentum ad hominem* or perhaps *ab homine/femine*. It makes an extreme claim to individuality whose accompanying strong feeling of freedom represents mere delusion. The extreme individualist is not claiming that some power of honesty or intellectual acuteness is operating, rather that him or her is what operates: "Trapped in the shameful prison of myself", each of us is the sole member of a unique species. Individuality is one thing, the notion that 'I do what I do because I is the is I is' is only the freedom of the feeblest excuses: and emphatically *not* what Macmurray means by 'personal'.

Noting his observation that by the 1970s the delusion of certainty had now attached itself to physical science's theories or mannerisms, one may see the same scientistic delusions in the 19th century: in so-called 'gross materialist' theories of an unconscious, sheerly physico-chemical reality; in social planning based on the associationist dogma of Bentham and Mill; and as the 8th Duke of Argyll complained in *The Reign of Law*, when such 'fixed laws' as Adam Smith plainly did not frame were cited at Westminster as *scientific proof* that social reform is wrong.

By the 1870s a movement certainly influential on Macmurray had got under way at Balliol College, Oxford, attacking such delusions. Its Scotophil radical Master, Benjamin Jowett, seems to have been aiming to turn

Macmurray in the 1960s (courtesy Duncan Campbell)

the place into a Scottish university – with the novelty for its day of promoting such extra-mural studies as Macmurray both promoted at Edinburgh University, and planned for as a Governor of Newbattle Abbey College. Such involvement in community work, social work studies, educational reform and the extension of access was carried on by followers of both Jowett's practice and Hegel's theory. To consider Hegel as Macmurray considered Karl Marx, bracketing out some aspects of his work as near superstition: one central intention is to overcome the errors from treating questions in artificial isolation from each other. Toiling to incorporate in vastly elaborated systematic work both the concerns of the humanities and such findings of science as there were in the early 19th century, Hegel and his contemporary Schelling inspired views of the unity of knowledge from points of view the in physical sciences.

In opposition to such views as well as in support of political liberalism, Jowett's students became Hegelians. Edward Caird was Professor of Moral Philosophy at Glasgow University in 1866, and his successor and disciple Sir Henry Jones continued a Hegelian teaching until 1921, through Macmurray's undergraduate day. One may see some mark of this school, regardless of his rejection of any belief that Hegel had worked out a system comprehending everything, in Macmurray's echoes of Jones. Trying to sum up his opposition to relativism Jones declares that freedom is to be governed by what is the case, scientific discovery is the self-disclosure of reality, reason the capacity for objectivity. Since no study short of the System of the Absolute comprehends reality, there is properly no such thing as science, says Jones. But the demonstrable truth of discoveries indicates that there *are*, in the plural, 'sciences': each marked out by the parts or aspects of reality comprising its province.

It would surely be hard to deny some lesson from Hegel in the paper Macmurray wrote in response to a putative dismissal of physical science's claim to knowledge heard at Oxford. The hypothetical knowledge which is all that is possible consists in an argued system of beliefs of a strictly provisional character. Far from its being given warrant of certainty by being scientific, its being scientific consists in its openness to considered revision. If Macmurray was elsewhere to relate the false dualism of knowledge and belief to the mediaeval case – indeed the *sundering* of science from philosophy dates from as late as Hegel's successors – he is quite clear that there is no knowledge which is not belief. You do not know anything unless you believe it. You do not know anything unless it is the case; you can have no absolute certainty nor should you seek it.

Macmurray's account of the theological doctrine of free will has been described by George Davie as weak, which it is as philosophy. It does however imply possession of a capacity for objective discrimination, of the characters of reality, things, characteristics, qualities far less problematic in relation to theories of ethical motivation. Macmurray's approach to religion and to personal relations is not, in the aesthetic misapprehension of what science is, counter to science. Rather is it precisely scientific, if not that reflective activity called science. Sir Karl Popper applauds Macmurray's identification of Christianity as the mainspring of science, the genuine basis of scientific knowledge is undivided awareness. As independent investigations certain sciences have to exclude from their method different aspects of that reality of which the individual is aware. That they do not in turn become compartmentalised, and do not stay quiet where they might inform and criticise, is as important as that their method does not ride roughshod where it merely confuses. The properly experimental life is the life which is not disorganised, which like scientific experiment is not random, has checks and must be susceptible of producing observations while not disdaining risks. Macmurray is offering no prescription aesthetic or otherwise, rather is he discussing something which is not passivity.

In the sometime highly influential metaphysics of F H Bradley, there is the conception of an Absolute in which all differences vanish, and in relation to which all workaday conceptions are incompletely true. Bradley's Absolute is allegedly experienced by sheer feeling, uncontaminated by thought. Whereas for him as for the Hegelian every statement falls short of truth, by failing to express the whole, or absolute, for Caird and Jones the absolute was not according to Bradley: the distinct and separate does not lose definition in 'the absolute', rather moral activity is taken up by it: differences do not disappear, there is rather an individuation. This individuation is not of some supposed fixed timeless being, but of an agency. It is a fact of active doing which is not as in Bradley 'experience of…', but rather participation *in* the Absolute. Allied to a notion of man's God-given mission in the world, this very optimistic view surely owed much to the observation that hitherto apparently irremediable squalor and poverty were being remedied at the time (a sort of 'verification' in history referred to by Macmurray). A notion of 'citizenship' is now being revived by students of the Hegelian group Caird and Jones belong to. Macmurray's cultural analyses have a great deal to offer it. The citizen studies self and society, action is duty.

Caird's is very much a philosophy of process, worked out in face of attempts to trace an importance for ethics in Darwinian or evolutionary theory. The blurb to Professor Duncan's book contrasts Macmurray's view of the human being with an alternative question, "are men merely animals with highly developed brains?" If human valuations are to be set at nothing, what is evolution?

Recent unpublished researches by Gael Turnbull add instructive footnotes to Caird, very notably the extent to which Caird was involved in discussions with the great Scottish theologian John McLeod Campbell, whom Macmurray may well of course have read. Indeed the account of Macmurray's religious development in *Search for Reality* encapsulates a movement from acceptance of ratiocinatory dogma by way of a shocked re-reading of the New Testament to a 'meaning of Christianity' view like Edward Caird's: in short the liberation of the Scottish church from Stoic legalistic perversions of Calvin which had bound it from the 17th century. McLeod Campbell had a notion of 'discussion' as an irreplaceable method of discovery very consonant with Macmurray's reflections on Language and interpersonal communication. McLeod Campbell is also worth noting among liberal Christians during the later Victorian challenge to faith in arguing the consonance with Christianity of science.

It is not paradoxical to refer Macmurray to David Hume, certainly in Norman Kemp Smith's exposition of Hume. The contemporary scholar James Noxon makes a point which indirectly relates the two: whereas after the public unsuccess of his large philosophical *Treatise and Enquiries* Hume has been said to have abandoned the study for the writing of essays, Noxon indicates how far these later works were a continuation of the initial enterprise. Those who might doubt that Macmurray's books are a similar venture to the later Hume might be shown how far, without pretension to achievements of the young Hume, Macmurray relates them to earlier work by others.

Following the experimental methods of the physical sciences Newton or Boyle pioneered, Hume investigated man, criticised current theory and analysed practice. If reason is capacity for objectivity, wordplay in Macmurray's title *Reason and Emotion* points to what that term has also been used to denote: a cat's cradle of obsessional ratiocinations in face of which one's senses and feelings have, uncorrected, to be denied. Hume's point is that such systematics (Kemp Smith recognises that the theology Hume knew was of this kind) are merely means by which deluded beings sustain their unquestioning. The sway of ratiocinatory schemes in modern anti-humanism is striking. One should not utterly distrust the senses, or the beliefs one finds forming in oneself. Some may be very sound. In fact only such beliefs can motivate, the statement that Reason is the slave of "the Passions" means that reason has no motivating power. As Scots from

Croom Robertson to John Anderson have insisted, this doesn't mean that one has an automatic bias or that truth is impossible. It insists rather on recognising a desire for truth which developmental psychologists well enough relate to an animal situation. Certain needs to 'find out' attain to an autonomy in man, just as Macmurray is plain that fear does.

Disastrously for cultural analysis, Christianity tends these days to be rejected as a mere imposition on essentially good, natural man. Hume had a conviction as to an efficacy of natural forces belonging with his day's optimistic view of nature. In view of the character of the systematics he deplored, he set in opposition to them a 'nature' which fosters human morality and affections in the cradle and in the family. Consonant with his own cult of nature he attempted to foster a preference for what he termed the calm passions, mollifying the savage ones. Hume's 'nature' was an interpretation of virtue, but reference to nature's arbitration raises all too easily the problem of dualism. Cults of the natural versus the non-natural have arisen, such as that described in Janko Lavrin's book on Nietzsche. The upshot is not merely the abstractly generalised 'animal' ideal, extolled as a religion.

As against this, Macmurray's ideas can have no superiority by virtue of their greater straightforwardness. They can be superior only by dint of soundness. His account of 'the personal' relates not to interhuman relations attempting to be mutually pleasing, but as a way of not avoiding the problem. In his useful pamphlet *John Macmurray in a Nutshell* D A S Fergusson refers to Macmurray as engaging in "a conceptual analysis of action". This is wrong! Macmurray treats of what he in a special sense terms 'action' as an operation which he discerns as going on in the world. He is saying that people can act according to what is the case.

Not that they always do. Further to this he ventures certain ideotypal characterisations of human behaviour: the tribal, which rejects change and suggested improvement because no purpose is seen in change. Beside this is the stoic, which continually refers to external standards and laws; and the organic, which apperceives in narrow aesthetic terms of what non-human nature does. Macmurray's analysis of the life which mankind has achieved involves account of a culture, and 'religion', which has transcended these patterns of domination or unfreedom. A great argument for his future relevance is that his criticisms identify characteristics of modern habits of mind, and ideologies, to the extent of demanding further exposition. Have not the humanities fallen into a tribal habit of organic preferences in conduct, even the conduct of elaborating stoic ideologies alleged to underlie, though they argue counter to, most actual human dealings with other humans?   *Robert Calder*

SCOTLAND'S QUALITY THEATRE QUARTERLY

COMPLETE PLAYSCRIPT / LIVELY DEBATE / IN-DEPTH INTERVIEWS

Brian Cox reads

theatre

SCOTLAND

so should YOU!

I wish to subscribe to *THEATRE SCOTLAND*, starting from the NEXT ISSUE /

CURRENT ISSUE* (delete as applicable) . I enclose a cheque payable to *THEATRE*

SCOTLAND for £   £13 for four issues, (£20 overseas surface / £30 airmail)

NAME   . . . .

ADDRESS   . . . .

. . . .

THEATRE SCOTLAND, 9a ANNANDALE STREET, EDINBURGH EH7 4AW

Macmurray's Religious Philosophy

A.R.C. Duncan

Rebelling against the theoretical and egocentric tradition of western philosophy, Macmurray claimed that philosophy must rethink its position. Instead of starting from the Cartesian 'I think', it must build on the Kantian primacy of the practical and start from the 'I do' of action. In developing a philosophy of action he hoped to provide a foundation on which could be erected a concept of the personal which would do justice to the value which we claim to put upon persons. From his first published paper of 1926 up to his death in 1976 he devoted his immense energies to the task of expounding what he called his philosophy of the personal. The driving force behind all his philosophical activity was however a deep-rooted conviction that the reality which he as a philosopher sought to find and to express in language was ultimately to be located in religion; he himself characterised his philosophical activity as a 'search for reality in religion'.

The rise of science has implied to many people a world view incompatible with that traditionally held by religion. In an empirically-minded age the validity of religion has been thought to rest on evidence provided by special types of religious experience granted only to a minority of people. From quite early days Macmurray was deeply troubled by the mediaeval attempt to reach a synthesis of Christian thought and Greek philosophy. Within western philosophy itself the long argument initiated by Descartes has moved, he claimed, steadily in the direction of atheism. Given its initial starting point, the *cogito*, this seemed to him inevitable. On the other hand, he added, "the view that there is no path from common experience to a belief in God ... seems to me hardly credible".

How then did Macmurray attempt to tackle this situation? We may begin with what he has to say about the nature of faith – which he sharply distinguished from belief. By belief he meant the attitude of mind adopted towards the propositional content of what are technically known as creeds, groups of statements in which theologians have attempted to formulate either the basic historical facts on which a given religion rests, or the minimum number of spiritual truths which describe the essence of the religion. Membership of a religious sect has often been made to depend officially on willingness to subscribe to the contents of the creed in the sense of making a public statement of belief. It is unfortunate that this intellectual, almost metaphysical exercise – it is extremely difficult honestly to profess belief in propositions which baffle the understanding – has been confused with the rather different concept of faith.

Unwilling as a philosopher to get entangled with dogma in any form, and offering no comments on the variety of such creeds, Macmurray interpreted the concept of faith by studying the way in which the word 'faith' was commonly used by the founder of the Christian religion as reported in the earliest documents. These studies were carried out in the early 1920s. In a radio talk of 1964, after emphasising the word 'faith' as a keyword in the Christian tradition, Macmurray described how he had read through the synoptic Gospels noting every occasion of its usage.

> The first thing I discovered was that Jesus habitually used the word "faith" without reference to an object. He would say, "Why have you no faith?" or "Your faith has saved you". There was no suggestion anywhere that faith referred to things that people believed or did not believe. It clearly had nothing to do with doctrines or creeds ... Now I found this surprising. I myself habitually thought of faith as referring to what Christians believed. One's faith, I thought, was expressed in a creed.

Pointing out the obvious fact that the contrast between faith and reason, inherited from the middle ages, is nowhere to be found in the teaching of Jesus, he stressed the other, even more significant contrast which *is* to be found in His teaching, the contrast between faith and fear:

> To have faith means not to be frightened. In that case faith must mean something like courage or confidence or trust.

And just as faith is not spoken of as having a specific object, so also there is no reference to an object of fear. The contrast is then interpreted by Macmurray as a contrast between two persisting and general attitudes of mind which may characterise a human being's life as a whole. To live in fear is constantly to be on the defensive towards life and towards other persons: to live in faith is to see life as offering endless opportunities, and other persons as potential friends.

As an enthusiastic student of natural science – indeed Macmurray at one time wanted to become a scientist – it is not surprising to find (a) that he became an early contributor to what is now known as philosophy of science, and (b) that he could see no necessary conflict between science and religion. In his rethinking of philosophy of science he pointed out that the impressive progress of natural science was due not only, as is so often stressed, to its abandonment of the qualitative physics of Aristotle in favour of the quantitative methods of Galileo and Newton, but much more to its abandonment of the search for certainty: a search which has for so long bedevilled western epistemological thought. Instead of searching, in the manner of Descartes, for what we might call hard lumps of indubitable knowledge, science in Macmurray's words substituted

> a belief which is uncertain and insecure, and proposed neither to throw it overboard nor to accept it, but to use it as basis for an experiment. Its fundamental principles become working hypotheses which form the starting points of a method which is deliberately designed for their own expansion and modification or even their rejection. So science offers us not demonstrated truth but a part in a drama ... of intellectual development that works by faith and hope.

The fact that the history of science is littered with abandoned theories Macmurray interprets as a sign of the strength of its faith, which has made it one of the greatest of human achievements.

In an early, intriguingly-titled paper 'Christianity – Pagan or Scientific' (1926) Macmurray concludes by suggesting that Christianity should itself become scientific: in the sense of

> living experimentally, holding all its doctrines as liable to modification or

even rejection, accepting all its rules of organisation and its laws of conduct as simply so much result of human experience to be used as working hypotheses and experimented with incessantly for their own development...

In this early paper Macmurray also suggests that religious development may possibly be in a state analogous to scientific development before the time of Galileo, and that fascination with the exciting progress of science has caused us to allow serious religious development to stagnate. Instead of living in a post-Christian era, Macmurray wondered whether we may be living in a *pre*-Christian era. His linking of scientific and religious faith led him to make the paradoxical and provocative remark that natural science is the most characteristically Christian thing in the modern world.

Let us now consider his view that belief in God as a supreme reality lay at the centre of all religion. In the first place, he distinguished between belief in God, and belief in the belief in God. It has been said that even if there were no such being as God, it is a good thing that people should believe in God, such belief acting as a powerful sanction for law and morality and being good for the human spirit. This attitude puts belief in God on the level of political propaganda, like the attitude adopted in Karl Marx's interpretation of early human history: before modern science rationalised the forces of nature it was both natural and necessary that men should believe in supernatural powers. Modern scientific knowledge will free us from the necessity of such beliefs, which properly belong to the period of mankind's immaturity. With such belief in the belief in God Macmurray had no sympathy at all. If there is no God, he declared, the effort to maintain and propagate religion is a crime against humanity.

What interested him was not the logical finding of a proof of the existence of God, but the real and dual problem of (a) reaching a conception of the nature of God which will not be manifestly false, inadequate, or meaningless, and (b) determining what it means actually to believe in God. The traditional proofs of the existence of God, so roughly treated by Kant, may have been and may still be excellent exercises in the intricacies of conceptual thought, but as has long been recognised they have little to do with the kind of Being at the heart of religion. They are at best what H.H.Price called "clarifications of propositions which religious persons antecedently believe". At worst, as in Kant's moral argument for the existence of God in which God appears as a kind of Divine Paymaster, they are travesties of the religious consciousness. What stirred the emotions of awe and reverence in Kant was not the thought of a Divine Being but the sight of the starry heavens above and the thought of the moral law within.

In addition to this distinction between belief in God and belief in the belief in God Macmurray also distinguishes between pseudo-religion and genuine religion – a distinction analogous to that between such a pseudo-science as psychology, and a genuinely empirical science such as astronomy. Pseudo-religion can take an emotional or an intellectual form, the emotional form resting on the dominance in human life of the emotion of fear. Unlike animal fear, which appears in connection with immediate danger, human fear can pervade our whole consciousness. It is symbolised by the greatest of all fears, the fear of death. One consequence of our human rationality is that we know, here and now, that some day in the future we shall die. Paradoxically human life has to be lived in the light of the knowledge of death, and Macmurray held strongly that until we explicitly and fully recognise this fact and come to terms with it, we cannot begin really to live. As a motive to action fear is negative and inhibiting and expresses itself in a sense of constraint rather than freedom, and in a sense of isolation rather than community. Macmurray does not deny the obvious fact pointed out by another Scottish philosopher, Norman Kemp Smith, that "fear is an essential element in our make-up ... and is the basis of all reflection, of all caution and care in action; of reason itself therefore". It is only when fear is allowed to become dominant that it becomes negative and evil. Pseudo-religion tends to offer salvation from fear through the attempt to deny the reality of death, to suppress the knowledge that we actually have of its inevitability.

This may be achieved through a doctrine of the immortality of the human soul, the kind of doctrine which has its most famous exposition in Plato's *Phaedo*, and by way of a further identification of *real* life with that which will be enjoyed after we have completed life in this world here below. Those who accept this doctrine can then obtain comfort and consolation for the pains of this life with the thought of joys to come. Also, as the Marxist thinker does not fail to point out, they need not be worried overmuch about improving the earthly conditions under which the vast majority of mankind has to live. Moreover, in dealing with the new fears which can come along with the steady increase of knowledge, pseudo-religion can choose the path of reaction. This is in effect an attempt to escape from the human world of knowledge and responsible personal action, to a lower type of animal existence which has no knowledge, to the world of the primitive, to that of childhood, to the craving to return to nature. When new knowledge appears we never know where it will lead us, so that it always represents a step into the unknown – we might almost call this the paradox of knowledge. Pseudo-religion has frequently in the past attempted to meet new knowledge by a reactionary return to old established truths, by an emphasis on the past rather than a courageous facing of the present and the future.

Intellectual pseudo-religion Macmurray regards as a serious enemy of genuine religion. He calls the form it takes idealism. Whereas the word 'idealism' is used in many different ways – indicating one or several schools of philosophy, or referring to a general attitude to life – Macmurray uses it to indicate the tendency to value ideas before things, and to value all activities concerned with ideas more than activities concerned with real things. The notion that knowledge is worth pursuing for its own sake instead of as a component in rational action is an example of an idealist attitude which has had effects in our educational practices which are perhaps not entirely beneficial. The ancient Greek exaltation of the theoretical life over the banausic life of those engaged in making or doing things provides another obvious example. In the field of religion it tends to express itself through a dualism of the life of the body and the life of the spirit, with the consequent identification of religion with the life of the spirit. This in turn becomes connected with the other dualism of 'this world' and 'the world beyond' in which reality is predicated of the world beyond. The Kingdom *of* Heaven becomes, as Macmurray once put it, the Kingdom *in* Heaven – the difference between two little prepositions representing an enormous difference in religious attitude.

What Macmurray sees as wrong with idealism is that it represents a serious misconception of the nature and function of ideas. It is of the nature of ideas to refer beyond themselves to the real world. That is their proper function. Ideas as such belong to the realm of the imagination where we can do as we please with them; but the important question about ideas is whether they are true or false. The answer to that can be determined only by going beyond them to actual experience in which we encounter real things and real people. The real world, the one in which we have to live, contains all manner of different entities. It contains intractable material objects which hinder our movement, and obstinate people who insist on going their own way and so frustrating our desires and intentions. To take refuge from this difficult real world in the more easily controllable world of ideas becomes only too tempting.

It is a natural consequence that our ideas about the world tend to become better and more satisfactory than reality. Gradually our ideas become *ideals* in terms of which we judge the unsatisfactory nature of the real world. An ideal is either an idea of how life might be or ought to be lived, or an idea of a better world which we should prefer to inhabit. It becomes vital here to distinguish between an ideal, which belongs to the world of ideas, and an intention, which belongs to the world of reality in which we have to act. People may of course try to realise their ideals, and many splendid achievements are the outcome of such attempts, but there is nothing in the nature of an ideal which compels us to try to realise it.

Idealists, Macmurray claims, tend to be divided against their selves, for they live in two worlds, and this can easily tend toward self-deception. An idealist type of religion must also be a religion of two worlds, the real world of things and people, and the world of the imagination, and so it must carry within itself the seeds of pseudo-religion. Macmurray in his search for true religion concluded that it must be an activity which takes place in the actual world in which we live, the world in which there are both real things, pleasant and unpleasant, and real people, obstinately self-centred or co-operatively neighbourly.

Before confronting Macmurray's conception of real religion, it may be instructive to compare the views of Whitehead, the self-styled philosopher of the organic, with Macmurray, the philosopher of the personal. Whitehead has the famous phrase, "religion is what a man does with his solitariness", a phrase based on his view that religion is the art and theory of the internal life of man, and that it is connected with what he calls "the awful, ultimate fact, which is the human being consciously alone with itself, for its own sake". Maintaining – a curious claim – that the Bible marks the coming of rationalism into religion, Whitehead is explicitly anxious to reject the view that religion is primarily a social fact, claiming that "it exhibits the note of progressive solitariness in the religious idea".

Although Whitehead's phrases have a striking and memorable ring to them, they do not always bear close scrutiny. There are so many things an individual might do in solitude which are not in any sense religious. For some human activities solitariness is essential – the creating of great poems like the Divine Comedy, the philosophical thinking that went to the writing of Kant's great *Critiques* – but these would not normally be described as religious activities. The claim that the Bible represents the note of progressive solitariness I find excessively difficult to reconcile with the commandment to love one's neighbour: an activity which cannot be performed in solitude. It would appear that Whitehead's concept of religion illustrates the individualism which has been rampant in western civilisation since the Reformation.

Macmurray would emphatically agree that religion is a personal affair, but he is careful to point out that he means 'personal' in the sense of the adjective for the noun 'person', and not 'private'. In developing his metaphysics of the personal, Macmurray quickly realised that persons can exist as persons only in mutuality. The fundamental unit in the field of the personal, he claimed, is never 'I' but 'I and you'. The self conceived as thinking subject standing over against the world as object is indeed solitary and can never achieve the level of the personal. To so consider the self is to generate insoluble puzzles about knowledge of other selves. The self, conceived as agent involved in dynamic relation with that which is other than the self, necessarily participates in the life of the world, the world of nature and the world of persons. Since he holds that the human being becomes a person only in relation to other persons, that mutuality is of the essence of the personal, we must expect Macmurray to say about religion things very different from those said by Whitehead.

Pointing out that religion in one form or another is the oldest and most characteristic mode of human life, Macmurray asks, "what is it that human beings express always and everywhere in their religious activities?" His reply is that "they express their sense of community; and therefore all religion is the expression of community". At this point it is essential to take into account Macmurray's distinction between 'society' and 'community'. What he calls 'society' exists wherever there is a group of people standing in functional relations to one another, whereas 'community' exists only where relations between people are genuinely personal relations. Macmurray might then join with Whitehead in denying that religion is a social activity, while affirming that it is a communal and personal activity. Primitive religion, which often includes ancestor worship, expresses the sense of community of the whole tribe, past, present and future. The Church of Rome at one time expressed the sense of community throughout European Christendom. With the growth of nationalism different nations tended to set up their own churches, each serving to express its sense of national community. Macmurray held that the Christian religion, which grew out of the Hebraic community of the chosen people, developed through the teaching of Jesus into a truly universal religion seeking to achieve and express the sense of community of mankind as a whole under the Fatherhood of God. He saw the task of the Christian church as being that of breaking down

> the exclusiveness which limits actual community to groups which are less than the whole of mankind, and its religious enemies are precisely those national religions, those limited and exclusive communions, which refuse to give place to the universal community and which resist the integration of humanity into a single communion.

For this reason Macmurray interprets the history of Christianity, which he refuses to identify with any one so-called Christian church or group, in terms of "a historic continuity of intention and purpose", the intention to achieve universal community.

In Macmurray's epistemology immediate experience is the normal direct form of human experience, and we withdraw into reflective experience usually because something has gone wrong and we need to discover some way of putting it right, or because we wish to give expression to some aspect of it. As a form of reflective experience religion is about personal relations, its language is the language of personal relations, its function the dual task of extending the sense of human community and of seeking to heal those breaches in personal relations which are the causes and sources of so much human sorrow and tragedy.

Thinking of religion as an all-inclusive form of human reflective experience, Macmurray never tired of insisting that serious religious activity must refer to reality. His identification of religion as the world of personal relations clearly stems from his reflection on the Hebraic-Christian tradition. If the whole law and the prophets indeed hang on the two commandments to love God and to love one's neighbour, and if love is realisable only as a form of relation between persons, then personal relations must be what Christian religion is about. Hence to attempt to find the reality of religion either in a supernatural world or in the inner spiritual life is to deny the importance of love and to condemn religion to function at the outer periphery of human concern instead of at the centre.

Turning from religion to theology, I should like to conclude by drawing attention to just three points in Macmurray's thinking about the idea of God. First, he rejects any thinking about God which attempts to answer the question, does God exist? In keeping with his revolutionary call to think from the standpoint of the self as agent in dynamic relation with the Other (his preferred word for the not-self) and therefore experiencing existence, Macmurray claimed that the real task is to reach an adequate conception of the religious term 'God'. To start with 'Does God exist?' presupposes that we have the idea and are looking for something corresponding to it, whereas the real problem is to formulate the idea.

Secondly, if we ask about God as an object of worship, then Macmurray remind us that we talk about various objects of worship: we may worship fame, money or even the State; that which we worship is that for which in *actual practice* we have an absolute reverence. But reverence can be misplaced. "The religious term 'God' is the name for the proper object of reverence", and that, Macmurray contends, must have at least the two characteristics of being above us, beyond our control and comprehension, and also of being congruous with our nature as persons. Since the personal is the highest category we know, God must be conceived as at least in some sense personal, and is referred to by Macmurray as 'the infinite of personality'. The pictorial language of ordinary religion and the abstractions of theology have for centuries attempted to stamp this into our ordinary consciousness, which is why we hear it said that we can express our love for God most fully through loving our neighbour.

Thirdly, Macmurray formulates the central theological problem in terms of his philosophy of action in this way: "Is the universal Other, from which the community of persons distinguishes itself, and which is the same for all persons, a personal or an impersonal Other?" The difference between a personal and an impersonal conception of the world is basically the contrast between the scientific and the religious modes of apperception. Scientific apperception is impersonal and pragmatic. It seeks knowledge of the world which is out there independent of us, and through the knowledge science gains we can use things in the world as instruments in fulfilling our intentions. Religious apperception is personal and communal and is the mode through which we reach the full expression of our rationality in our personal relations with other persons. Human beings require both religion and science, and any adequate philosophy of human existence must develop categories which enable it to recognise the reality and importance of both of the two kinds of knowledge of which human beings are capable, the objective impersonal knowledge of the world, acquired by science, and the personal knowledge we have of one another which makes life worth while.

In all his thinking about science, art and religion Macmurray kept insisting that we must constantly remind ourselves that these are not abstract ideas but things human beings do. Human beings acquire factual knowledge, human beings make and enjoy works of art, human beings enter into personal relations and in each field they meet with varying degrees of success and failure. But all are reflective activities and therefore they must start from and return to immediate experience, the experience of actual living. Human life is a constant rhythm of withdrawal into reflection and return to the world of action. This is why Macmurray does not deny that in religion there is an inner spiritual life which requires to be cultivated, he simply insists that it must resist the tendency towards dualism and strive rather to find its reference in this world:

> ... it is one thing to say that religion is about another world. It is a very different thing to say that it is about an aspect of this world to which we are usually blind. The first statement is a falsification of religion which makes it unreal. The second is the truth of real religion.

A. R. C. Duncan

Christine McNeill

Shadow Play

He watched from the window with a cup of tea.
Van Gogh's *Peach Trees in Blossom near Arles*
was on his mind, or Munch's *Music in the Street.*
It was his habit to start the day by asking questions
about art. The blue and coal tits harlequined
from twig to twig. He raised the sash,
put breadcrumbs on the window ledge.

One day he fell for a darker version:
"In 1980, there was a war in Afghanistan", he said,
hands and knees on the living-room carpet.
"This year there is a war in Bosnia–Herzegovina."
He slapped down his hand: "Hundreds, thousands, millions."
Mumbling about the inter-connectedness of life,
he pursued the fleas with an axe day and night.

In hospital she brought him her defeat:
a cake, wrapped in foil.
She told him of a candle she had lit.
The wax had spread into a half-circle.
All sorts of landscapes
kindled in her voice
strategically placed to deny his depression.

A lamp glared on his shadow-playing fingers.
A tree grew on the wall. A rabbit chased a bird.
"Madness", he said, "begins in the flesh",
and snatched something off his leg.
Immersed it in a glass of water.
Day and night she saw it wriggling;
thought of people, and absence.

Viennese Still Life

This gallery has been his ground
of natural limits. From the radiator
he ruminates on Spinoza's theory:
whether short- or far-sighted
one can break the light.

The Japanese walk in
as into an eating bowl.
Searching behind the varnish
for something more than paint.
The walls are full of limbs.

In 1940 he was a bomber pilot.
At night he played God with "Christmas
trees"; flares that he threw down
to illuminate a town or village
before attacking it.

The floor creaks.
The Japanese bow
before the pictures' signatures.
Art to him, is a mixed marriage of trees.
Pink and clean, the bodies belong to no one.

Transient

A Korean sect predicted
the world would end last Wednesday.
The tramp took it in his stride.
Retrieving wellies from a dustbin,
then walking into a church.
Bravura arms of uncles and aunts
settled a Christening robe.
"A biblical name", the godmother said,
"is worth its weight in gold",
and saw the tramp's blue eyes
handling cradle, staff, and cross.
She hastily stroked the child's head,

conceiving a red-brick house,
an iron horse-shoe encircling its number.
A father. A husband. A lover.
"I christen you John, Andrew, Simon..."
The names took the air with swords.
The baby screamed,
as though it were pulled
through wheels.
The tramp nodded.
The names would endure
like those saints on high windows
singing praises to the night.

Transmigration

My landlord said that my kitchen
window would be painted.
I asked the workmen if I could leave
my indoor window-box. He said no.
The window must be open,
for the two sashes need to cross each other.
All summer the fuchsia has mingled with the ivy.
When I remove the box, blossoms
that would have stayed till November,
drop, like discarded gems.

The shock on hearing
that a friend had killed himself.
His wife had locked all windows
but when she returned from identifying him,
there was a bird in the kitchen.
It had nibbled an apple,
drunk water from a bowl.
When the window was lifted,
it did not flutter around fixtures,
but flew straight out.

October air chills.
White paint is dry.
I heave the window box back on the sill.
She asked: "How much do I create my own reality?"
He'd said to her:
"How lovely the vine leaves are this autumn",
and put a dark grape on her tongue.
She didn't bite into it immediately.
Control, she thought, was the best antidote
to swallows leaving for Africa.

Ruth McIlroy

Reading list

I am sitting beside the alarmed door
reading how the signs of drama create meaning;
over there, a man is patting another man's body
gently, but they are not friends;
I have the 6.30 am head, yawn,
find the City Ladies, try to follow
Tadeusz Kowzan's thirteen sign systems
and the six elements of Aristotle:
but flight BA 7213 is ready for boarding.
The air in the cabin is carefully controlled,
fasten the tapes round your waist like this,
the act of pulling the life-mask down
opens up the oxygen supply;
with greater clarity, Bazin speaks
of the dramatic element as interchangeable between arts;
here is a whistle for attracting attention
and I'd just like to add my personal welcome.
The meaning of verbal utterances
must always be analysed in dramatic context;
smoking is not permitted in the toilets
which as an added safety feature
have been fitted with automatic smoke alarms.
The landing music is a signal to be frightened;
drama is a mimesis of real life,
and contemporary semioticians work on
both the intellectual and the emotional plane.

Late germination

This pod is silky-light, and lost in air
through the dark ages, dries to husk
pinching in to the uttermost
its densest speck of grit, intensity
small as dust-mote, poor at heart
dark aril, helpless, indestructible.

Through time, intact, its genus long extinct
this seed may light upon the grace of water
and from millenia will rise a cryptogam
arcane configuration of stalk and blade
a botanical marvel, hieroglyph
signifying nothing but its particular joy.

Easter Saturday

After the darkness, there is a time of waiting
it is all we know of, or have,
and so we collect stones unhurriedly
Iona marble, cool as egg
stretches the moment with its whiteness
stretching out our poverty for the sun to curl
on this salt unbearable richness.

This is enough; perhaps someday there will be
a place with better light, but now
I recognise your desire to stay
beside this thin abandoned sea
where at least it is quiet and calm
and wonderfully warmer than yesterday.

Milano Centrale

Forget the station
(we have Mussolini to thank for it)
but this is the end of the line
there is nowhere better
I am out of stratagems

The men with cigarettes hover
I turn my back and crouch
they crawl and circle, mutter 'Caffé?'
my god, I am a child
in my cruel father's halls

And did I clench a fist
did I find a voice at last?
it was a violent place, father
harsh remedies

Driven out to the warm rain
I call down thunder
it is not enough
it is never, never enough.

Reviews

Critical Voices

Devolving English Literature, Robert Crawford, Clarendon ·Press, £10.95; *Reading Douglas Dunn*, ed Robert Crawford & David Kinloch, EUP, £14.95; *Iain Crichton Smith: Critical Essays*, ed Colin Nicholson, EUP, £14.95; *The Scottish Novel Since the Seventies*, ed Gavin Wallace & Randall Stevenson, EUP, £14.95; *The Arts of Alasdair Gray*, ed Robert Crawford & Thom Nairn, EUP, £16.95.

According to Robert Crawford in *Devolving English Literature*, as an academic discipline at least, "English Literature" was actually invented by a Scot, Hugh Blair. His *Lecture on Rhetoric and Belles Lettres* (1784) launched the subject at the University of Edinburgh. Since then, of course, the strange phenomenon of writers like James, Wilde and Stevenson as somehow belonging to "English Literature" has been widely accepted, even after T S Eliot had radically transformed our perception of at least its poetic tradition. And Eliot, of course, was an American. Blair's intention, in any case, was to make Scottish writing conform to English standards, a requirement not firmly rejected until MacDiarmid, for whom even Burns conformed too much to Anglocentric notions of poetry, hence his famous battle-cry, "Not Burns, Dunbar!"

Crawford examines how "English Literature" as an implicit system of values, imposed all kinds of cultural and linguistic constraints, not only to the Scots, Welsh and Irish, but also writers from the "provincial" England outside London and the Home Counties. Its influence also reached the furthest outposts of Empire, and later Commonwealth. Consequently far-reaching in its analysis, his book opens up new perspectives on such key figures, and "literary ambassadors" of Scotland to England, as Scott and Carlyle, and also the anthropologist James Frazer, a great influence on the Modernists. He also treats contemporary poets, such as Douglas Dunn and the Australian Les Murray, as heirs of the Modernists, whom Crawford regards as subverters of anglocentrism. Because of his deployment of demotic speech,

Dunn gets considerable coverage as a "modernist", but in this sense he is no more so than Robert Garioch and Sydney Goodsir Smith were, yet they are not discussed at all. As for novelists, Lewis Grassic Gibbon, as Crawford asserts, certainly counts as a "modernist", but so does Naomi Mitchison. Many of her historical novels, written at roughly the same time as Gibbon's *A Scots Quair*, such as *The Corn King and the Spring Queen* (1931), are just as much in tune with anthropological concerns in a "modernist" manner as anything written by Gibbon. Sydney Goodsir Smith also displayed modernist credentials in *Carotid Cornucopius* (1947), commended for its "awareness of James Joyce" by Hugh MacDiarmid. It may be relevant to note that none of these authors are likely to be familiar to English readers. Despite such omissions, however, *Devolving English Literature* triumphs as an acute analysis, based on hard historical evidence rather than vaporous literary theory, of how Scottish writers since MacDiarmid have reversed the legacy of Hugh Blair. Were Crawford's first four chapters not so meticulous in their historical and literary analysis, the final two, 'Modernism as Provincialism' and 'Barbarians' would have seemed merely provocative.

Barbarians (1979) is a Douglas Dunn title, sensitively analysed, together with *The Happier Life* (1972) and *Love or Nothing* (1974), by Bernard O'Donohue in 'Moving Towards a Vernacular of Compassion', his contribution to *Reading Douglas Dunn*. Equally sensitive, Paul Hamilton does full justice to *Elegies* (1985) in 'Writing with Light'. Robert Crawford on *Secret Villager* (1985) makes this claim: "Dunn's rich, sensuous phrase-making is excelled in twentieth-century Scottish verse only by that of MacDiarmid in the early Scots lyrics. Compared to his verbal gifts, the language of other modern Scottish poets seems often thin and dry." Sean O'Brien's bracing essay on 'Dunn and Politics' is more commendably earth-bound. His essay illuminates how exemplary an opponent of Thatcherite values the poet has been, without compromising, but actually enriching his art. Stimulating, but also exasperating, W N Herbert blazes the fireworks in 'Dunn and Dundee: Dunn's Reentry into Scottish Culture'. But the essays I enjoyed most, perhaps because both are skilfully concise, were Jane Stabler's biographical sketch, and Richard Price on 'Taking Exception: Douglas Dunn's Criticism'. As it includes everything (just about) written by and about the poet to date, James Kidd's bibliography is of permanent value.

Douglas Dunn's contribution to the volume of essays on Iain Crichton Smith is a generous tribute to a poet so strikingly different from him. In 'The Wireless Behind the Curtain', he pays him the following compliment: "In *The Village* (1989), unexpected lyrical phrasings occur with satisfying frequency. In the last lines of 'Listen', for example, the sociable and the numinous become part of the same voice." Furthermore, he declares, "No-one else in Scottish poetry creates such lines, phrases, and images, or releases a lyricism of the same kind of comparable rarity and excellence." *From Bourgeois Land* (1969) on the other hand, he calls "tetchily programmatic", as if the poet had later "outgrown" its raw anger. Lorn Macintyre is more even-handed about it, conceding that the poet "scrutinised modern Scotland, with dislike showing through every line" but also pointing out that "the writing of the sequence allowed Crichton Smith to scrutinise Scottish Highland society in an international context." Macintyre's essay, 'A Rare Intelligence', is particularly valuable for its excerpts from a 1971 interview during which Crichton Smith revealed: "In my poetry I want to struggle against the fact that the Highlander is naturally a nostalgic person, because he is living in a civilisation which sort of abnegates everything that he has ever stood for, and he thinks that he is finished as a being of the future, and that is tremendous, and Gaelic poetry is full of nostalgia." But Iain Crichton Smith cannot be fully understood without some inkling of his Gaelic poetry, which is incisively discussed by Derick Thomson. Sorley MacLean, in a brief but potent foreword, has this to say about the poems in both languages: "...the theme and attitudes are the same in English and in Gaelic. There is the same contemplation of the world *sub specie Lewisiana, sub specie mundi* and *sub specie aeternitatis*, the same pity and sympathy without condescension, the many-sided aspects of the human condition and dilemma, the same deep and far-ranging sympathies, the same modesty and sincerity." His varied achievements are further treated by Cairns Craig on 'The English Fiction', Richard A V Cox on 'The Gaelic Fiction', and Stewart Conn on 'The Radio Work'. Colin Nicholson on 'Deer on the High Hills' reads like a tour-de-force of critical explication which examines the long, meditative poem entirely in terms of what it reveals about the nature of language and metaphor. It is also discussed by Christopher Small in 'The White Horse: Design and Grace'. He points out that "The long 'meditation' *Deer on the High Hills*, though it appears to offer a symbolic account of poetic activity, strives to escape from symbols altogether." But it is George Watson in 'Double Man at a Culloden of the Spirit' who gets to the root of the Highland poet's appeal: "...an unflinching quality in Crichton Smith's imagination."

Douglas Gifford's essay 'The Fiction of Iain Crichton Smith' is one of the best contributions to *The Scottish Novel Since the Seventies*. Authoritative, occasionally provocative, the volume is a critical landmark, not just because the only one on the subject so far, but primarily because in the past 20 years or so Scottish novelists have been prolific and highly innovative. It implicitly makes a good case, too, that the Scottish novel has become very cosmopolitan, and superior to fiction south of the border. Paradoxically, despite such an explosion of creative energy and exuberance, Gavin Wallace can talk of 'The Novel of Damaged Identity' in the fiction of Brian McCabe, Ron Butlin and Janice Galloway, and Douglas Dunn in an essay on the 'Divergent Scottishness' of William Boyd, Allan Massie and Ronald Frame can start with this glum observation: "As is well known, Scotland is susceptible to self-inflicted disfigurement." Strong words, but more applicable to places like Yugoslavia I would have thought. In the case of Wallace, however, he does at least suggest that the very fact his chosen novelists deal effectively with much that is negative in the Scottish psyche may be a sign of self-analytical health. A similar perspective, but from another angle, is provided by Carol Anderson on women novelists in 'Listening to the Women Talk'. The seventeen items, all of great interest and value, include essays on Robin Jenkins, Muriel Spark, Iain Banks, and Emma Tennant. Alison Lumsden provides an invaluable bibliography, as well as an essay on 'Innovation and Reaction in the fiction of Alasdair Gray'. Gray also features prominently in Edwin Morgan's encyclopedic 'Tradition and Experiment in the Glasgow Novel.'

As for *The Arts of Alasdair Gray*, it trumps all the other books reviewed here because, generously illustrated, it is designed by Gray himself. Bruce Charlton's biographical sketch, 'The Story So Far' is a tribute to the man's persistence in the face of unfavourable financial circumstances. There are also essays by Cordelia Oliver on Gray as visual artist, Edwin Morgan on 'Gray and Glasgow', Thom Nairn on the poetry, and Randall Stevenson on 'Alasdair Gray and the Postmodern'. His intense topicality is demonstrated by Christopher Harvie on 'Alasdair Gray and the Condition of Scotland Question'. If one is to judge this book by its cover, the artist-novelist appears to regard all critics as wasps.   *Mario Relich*

Metrical Feet

Into the White World, Kenneth White, Scotsoun, £10.55; *Pilgrim of the Void,* Kenneth White, Mainstream, £14.99; *In The Palace Of Serpents,* Tom Pow, Canongate, £9.95; *The Golden Peak,* Kathleen Jamie, Virago, £14.99

So what about Kenneth White: is it hype or genius? He's not the most immediately striking writer – in the absence of conventional poetic devices, the simplicity of his written style can seem arid in shorter poems or didactic in longer, because he declines the semantic doubling which metaphor, for instance, facilitates. With White, a short poem is just that – expect no analogue. In the longer work, where a parallel might be a welcome companion in linear foraging, again it is only what it is – links beyond the text consist of references to other works and other thinkers, clearly given. Though this straightforward style might be assumed to avoid obscurity, nevertheless there are readers who claim to be mystified as to what Kenneth White is on about.

This may be because with White it isn't the surrogation of nouns that resonates in other places, it's his use of adjectives, which seem to imply much more than description. One senses a hinterland of meaning, as if it isn't the quantitative noun-thing that's important, but the qualities that thing embodies. Not the particularity of a single gull somewhere in the world, but its whiteness, its flight: universal gullishness. He isn't making the conventional metaphorical association between the disparate, but between the separate. By this stylistic means, White's work suggests Heraclitan images of paradoxic constant–change, of eternal recurrence within difference, a pre-Platonic unity of the ideal and the real that carries him, philosophically, Eastward.

The essential difference of this device from metaphor or simile, which suggest two different images and ask the reader to judge whether their juxtaposition is a harmonic correspondence, is that White offers only a single aspect, the long view through all the spheres in which a certain quality may occur. He asks the reader to say what the 'whiteness' of that gull is associated with, so that what it means becomes both mythic and personal – as it is, one assumes, for Kenneth White himself: the choice of the word 'white' as an example here is not coincidental. It is a favourite adjective, often occurring at climactic poetic moments of insight, as if he recognises himself in the world at that instant, a part of his own mythology.

The two items under review here show something of the roundedness of White's work. The Scotsoun cassettes feature a varied selection of his poetry, superbly voiced by the man himself, while *Pilgrim of the Void* shows him "under way", travelling the fabled country of the East for the first time, and ending in the Nipponese north of Basho. Both publications come highly recommended and, one feels, will be currency for a very long time. White's achievements are unquestionable, but still to be fully evaluated here. Scotland's welcome to its prodigal is rather muted, his questing is as yet somewhat misunderstood.

Tom Pow is a more rooted spirit, though nonetheless adventuresome: *In The Palace Of Serpents* is a powerful narrative, which after hiccuping at the outset with various strange fellows met en route, settles to a serious vein of thought on Peru in crisis. Pow's own naïvité attracts at first, as one by one his cosy illusions are shattered and he hardens to the tourist traps – though not before reaching the goal of his travail, Machu Picchu – a beautifully-sustained piece of writing where the landscape and the mind fuse, in "geo-poetic" fashion. Pow is a genial, concerned tourist who makes an ideal companion for an armchair odyssey. Whereas White in Japan is like following an expert checking the facts on the ground against those accumulated from study, Pow discovers himself as he unearths Peru. Otherwise their approaches are not so different: Pow, like White, sprinkles his own and other poets' work through the pages of his book, creating a sense of time as stopped in a place at the moment of writing or reading, and providing an angle on the narrative axis.

Kathleen Jamie, though a respected poet, has chosen to leave verse alone in *The Golden Peak*. This makes her book more novelistic than either White's or Pow's, the story of a young Scots woman befriending members of a Shi'i community in Northern Pakistan, and, on both sides, of learning to trust in strangers. Despite the form, Jamie's writing glows with poetry. She seems to have the knack of listening to what people actually say, rather than translating and honing in the process. The people she meets grow slowly in the imagination as familiarity increases. Her narrative winds around the characteristics of the speech she records, so that it echoes the Empire-English pidgin. Jamie, like Pow, is discovering herself as she goes, questioning Western feminist thinking and her Scottish tradition against a very different experience, in particular that of the Rashida, who seems to typify a contented woman.

Towards the end of *The Golden Peak*, Jamie records a lasting image of Rashida rising in the morning to her domestic routines, as the writer herself is underway on her travels again. Telling perhaps that Jamie, like Pow during his time on the island of Amantani, sees through the dusty hustle of the traveller's road to the heart of the native community when she stops in one place with a single family. Genuine affection develops for individual people, not just the culture-myth of the place – and that is a journey which takes longer than a two-week break in the sun, with no few vicissitudes en route.   *Robert Alan Jamieson*

Metrical Feats?

Aimed at Nobody, W S Graham, Faber, £5.99; *Selected Poems*, Kirkpatrick Dobie, Peterloo, £6.95; *Selected Poems*, Ken Morrice, Keith Murray, £6.95; *The Elementary Particles*, Gerry Loose, Taranis, £5.99

W S Graham, who died in January 1986 overshadowed by Larkin obituaries and post-Christmas torpor, has seemed fated to be sidelined, overlooked, simply unread. Beginning in the 1940s as an imitator of Dylan Thomas – when the great man was there to show the world how, and how hammily, it should be done – Graham published his first three slim volumes in 1942, 1944 and 1945, at a time when the world assuredly had other things on its mind. *The White Threshold* (1949) marked the emergence of a voice of his own, but it was not till *The Nightfishing* (1955) that he got fully into his stride and was seen as a distinctive writer with registers (and silences) that bore a unique imprint. After that he published no book until *Malcolm Mooney's Land* in 1970 – a pause so long that (so the story goes) even his publishers, Faber, guessed that he was dead. In his introduction to the book under review, Robin Skelton reports this more tactfully by saying "they had lost touch with him and did not know he was still writing". *Implements in their Places* followed in 1977 and the *Collected Poems* in 1979.

Aimed at Nobody collects fragments from notebooks and miscellaneous worksheets. The work in it was considered incomplete, or even discarded, by Graham himself; but the book's co-editor, his friend and (at *The Malahat Review*) publisher Robin Skelton, rightly judges that the poems are of interest for the light they shed on his collected work. And indeed there are beautiful poems here.

In one of the few important explorations of Graham's poetry, Calvin Bedient (in *Eight Contemporary Poets*) described him as "a tart mixture of the apparently naïve and the formidably knowing". He saw Graham's as "a poetry uniquely at bay" possessing "a daring that seems innocent of what it is", and noted that poetry's strength as a "refused power and glory". This is well put, and perfectly substantiated by one of the loveliest pieces in *Aimed at Nobody*, 'Myself the Day Desires', written in October 1969. The last two quatrains read:

> If while I tell you this you want
> To interrupt with your some question
> Think twice. The dear I am infant
> Has started out and he is gone
> Is gone on the blue rainlit road
> Away and away from what the words call
> Anything that I never could
> Have as my home at all.

There are points in these eight lines where a first reading is almost certain to stumble. Before "Think twice", for example, our ear is not likely to be prepared for so strong a line-end: the rhythm of what goes before, and the unpunctuated semblance of enjambement, encourage us to want to read on, but instead he enforces a pause that emphasises his injunction "Think twice". Along with the unanticipated tripwires, though, there are also modest rhythmic aids that strike me as unimprovable: the repetition of "is gone" is one of these, ballad-like, perilously close to sentimentality but still this side of it, heart-stopping.

Other poems that need no apology for being collected now certainly include 'More Shots of Mister Simpson' and 'The Conscript Goes'; in a future *Collected* it would be good to see the former printed after the latter where it belongs. But surely the poem in this book which proves Graham's lyric gift most cogently, and with that easily-worn joy and sadness that seem always to thread his work, is 'The Honey Game', with a glorious opening quatrain:

> Lightly the light. Let's try the Honey
> Game you and I are best at.
> Because I know you are broken
> I can put you together again.

It is a great pity that Graham's voice, so quiet, with the timbre of respect for the world's silences, should be going unheard by so many now, both in Scotland and, more broadly, wherever there are readers of postwar poetry in English. His influence now is virtually nil; yet his exactions and textural scruples could offer a salutary counter to some of the noisier products of our day.

Not that Kirkpatrick Dobie is noisy. Described on the cover as a retired grain merchant born in Dumfries in 1908, where, one year excepted, he has lived for all his life, he would better be described as sensitive yet firm. The personality that emerges in his *Selected Poems* is a thoroughly likeable one: wry, empirical, humorous, with a robust curiosity about his fellow-beings and a quality seldom mentioned nowadays, wisdom. The poems are about people and dogs, statues and the cinema, writers, towns, poppies in a field – it is all extremely civilised, and Kirkpatrick Dobie, if I read him correctly as a modest man, would himself be the last to imagine it is great poetry. Greatness isn't the point. The point instead is to enact affection. Dobie's poems are a way of making continuities in the world, and by successfully doing this they may matter more to many readers than many a poem that stands received aesthetics upside down and is acclaimed for doing it but doesn't necessarily have all that much to say. Dobie always has something to say, and he says it well – as in his rhythmically-perfect lines on his father, which conclude:

> I've never visited his grave.
> I couldn't stand and moralize
> or seem to take his size.
> What I remember doesn't lie
> in any cemetery.
> I have his stick
> rough-handled, thick,
> and now in my own wintry weather
> stumble or slip
> I feel his grip.

Ken Morrice, seemingly a tetchier personality, is a psychiatrist, and there are pieces in his *Selected Poems* that draw upon this experience directly. At times these poems draw a covert, understanding smile from Morrice, as when Archie, the hospital pig-man, fails to return his good-day:

> They insist he is deaf and dumb.
> But yesterday I heard him talking fondly
> to an attentive honking of pigs.
> Clearly he is choosy.

There is no attempt to enter imaginatively into the minds of the mentally-ill, though – no attempt such as Ken Kesey or Heiner Kipphardt made in fiction, or Selima Hill in poetry. Maybe Ken Morrice would argue that such an attempt would be presumptuous; but its absence seems also to argue a certain failure of sympathy. Perhaps it is only consistent, then, that some of Morrice's best writing is not about people but about landscape:

> Cattle steam in flooded fields
> That sodden until Pentecost
> Glitter like acres of the sea
> In whose green depths the sun is lost.

Gerry Loose, I'm afraid, struck me as a writer of an all too familiar kind. Plainly an affectionate, generous person, implicitly he thinks that good intentions make good poems. Unfortunately they don't. The love of landscape and the natural world that breathes of every page of *The Elementary Particles*, though an attractive human quality, is not in itself enough. Take these lines, for instance, from an eight-page poem about crows:

Lie or sit for hours on heath and moss
of a mountain bog
Two scald crows will be there but do not look at them
You can move but slowly
The crows will watch you
Enjoy yourself look at the distant mountains
how they fold into the west
watch the wind the sky
the rocks surround you
In time the crows will stop watching you
You may look at them

It would be so pleasant to be receiving letters from a Gerry Loose, or reading his journal, that I inevitably feel churlish if I complain when he casts his thoughts in poetry form. But his work has little conceptual energy, linguistic address, or sense of what poetry might expect of those who write it.   *Michael Hulse*

Sympathetic magic

Carmina Gadelica – Hymns and Incantations Collected in the Highlands and Islands of Scotland in the Last Century, Alexander Carmichael, ed John MacInnes, Floris, £11.99; *Scottish Customs from the Cradle to the Grave,* Margaret Bennett, Polygon, £9.95; *Galoshins – The Scottish Folk Play,* Brian Hayward, Edinburgh University Press, £40

In exploring different aspects of the Scottish experience, these three books illuminate the issue of national identity. *Carmina Gadelica*, or *Ortha nan Gaidheal*, is the definitive collection of Highlands and Islands incantations and hymns. Six volumes were published between 1910 and 1971; selections have appeared before – *The Sun Dances* (1940) and *New Moon of the Seasons* (1986). Although the original lacks music, arrangements include *St. Patrick's Breastplate* (1992) by Ellen Wycherley. MacInnes reprints the English texts and notes from volumes I–VI, omitting the Gaelic texts and glossary, as well as the folk type and motif index and most of the carefully-selected Celtic letters. Given the enthusiasm for Gaelic traditions of the original collector Alexander Carmichael, the losses are regrettable.

Graceful rhymes ritualise every aspect of life. There are prayers for rising, sleeping, justice and love; charms for protection against fairies. Rhythmic chants animate work from herding to waulking. The perceived power of words, characteristic of oral tradition, is evident. A benevolent God is ever-present: "God with me lying down,/ God with me rising up,/ God with me in each ray of light". Saints, biblical and apocryphal figures are invoked. In a milking croon: "Come, beloved Colum of the fold,/ Come great Bride of the flocks,/ Come, fair Mary from the cloud". Apparently Highland cows would not give milk without hearing their favourite songs. There is a wealth of such contextual detail about customs, beliefs and informants.

Social mores are emphasised through verse, creating a community of mutual obligations. The woman donning her kertch (adult headdress) for the first time is advised: "Be thou hospitable, yet be wise,/ ...Be thou exact, yet generous". Natural and supernatural are linked by sympathetic magic:

The charm placed of Columba
About the right knee of Maol Iodha,
Against pain, against sting, against venom,
Against tooth disease, against bodily disease.

Cultural harmony, and the 'uncomplaining' industry of Highlanders, is emphasised as they are bracketed with classical pastoral societies (a commonplace in Scottish thought from the Enlightenment on), and the noble savages of Africa. Born in Lismore and employed as a Customs and Excise Officer on Skye, Uist and Barra, Carmichael presented his people in the best possible light, as he saw it. In a period of social change he was no mere salvage folklorist: he was active in Highland land reforms, and his literary achievements were recognised by a Civil List pension and honorary LL.D. Initially well-received, *Carmina* aroused controversy. MacInnes detects "editorial repairwork", especially on 'Invocation of the Graces', although the "core" is oral tradition.

Margaret Bennett's *Scottish Customs* utilises oral and written texts in English and Gaelic, and photographs, to document rites of passage and personal customs from 1549 to 1992. In addition to its ethnographic value, *Scottish Customs* is hugely entertaining. Audrey Bain, for instance, describes "Jumping the Chanty" in Kilmarnock, a po adorned with rhymes: "Two white pillows edged with lace,/ Bride and bridegroom face to face,/ Everything in its proper place,/ TALLY HO!!!" In a skilful interview with Margaret Ann Clouston (born 1880 on Orkney) Bennett draws out a first-hand account of traditional midwifery: cutting the umbilical cord with unsterilised scissors and putting burnt cloth on the new-born's navel.

Certain customs recall the *Carmina*. For instance, the Rev. James Napier recalled (1879) being a childhood victim of the evil eye. An old woman bathed his hands and feet with salt water, ritually prepared; Napier drank this three times. After 'scoring aboon the breath' (drawing her finger across his brow) she used a formula, 'Guid preserve me frae a' skaith'. Bennett innovatively, and sensitively, includes four accounts of her grandfather's burial, the last 'walking funeral' in Uig. Iain Johnston, a cultural 'outsider' from Glasgow explains: "everyone in the village, relatives, the lot, all mixed together and helped." There is a pervasive sense of community here, sustained by shared traditions.

This is an invaluable reference volume, with one reservation. No mention is made of Jewish-, Italian-, Irish- or Asian-Scottish customs. Unfortunately, given its publication date, *Scottish Customs* could not take account of excellent recent studies like Bashir Maan's *The New Scots* (1992)

Brian Hayward focusses on one calendar custom: *Galoshins* in Scotland c. 1700 to 1988. The play was performed by bands of guisers during Hallowe'en and Yuletide, traditionally times of licensed misrule. Over two thirds of the book is 'The Gazetteer': a compendium of all known texts – many previously unpublished – and commentary.

The title is ingeniously interpreted, citing Dunbar and Scott, as related to peasants' clogs; giving of footwear (glaschane) to the poor (guisers) bringing luck to the donor. Galatian faces an enemy: Alexander of Mac-

edon, Hector, William Wallace, or King George. National pride is often expressed at this point. In the Bowden play of 1815:

Here comes I, Alexander of Macedon
Who conquered the world, all, but Scotland alone,
And when I came to Scotland
My heart it grew cold, my heart it grew cold
To see that little nation, sae crowse and sae bold.

Galatian is killed in combat, and often renamed Jack, the slayer's brother. The victim is revived by a Doctor who applies 'hoxy croxy' to 'nose and bum'. The brothers are reconciled. Followers – 'Wee Johnny Funny ... the man that takes the money' – make a collection, and there is a final song.

The text, Hayward suggests, reflects Winter and Summer king combats, the Celtic Isle of the Blest and characters like the Healer Fool. *Galoshins* is plausibly explained as an offshoot of feudal society, losing relevance with industrialisation. This begs the question of why the play survived in Biggar. Cross-cultural comparisons would be useful. Hayward acknowledges customs akin to Galoshins, including Belsnickling (Nova Scotia), Mumming (Newfoundland) and the Mummers Play (England). Similar plays have been recorded in Shetland. A speculative parallel might be drawn between 'Big Head and Little Wit' of Auchinleck and 'Giants and Big Heads' in Andalusian procession. The last-mentioned, with phallic *porra* (clubs), dissipates tensions between classes and generations.

These books make fascinating texts accessible, showing individual, place and community as integrated through their narratives, customs and beliefs.   *Valentina Bold*

Classical Scots Abroad

Tales Frae the Odyssey o Homer, William Neill, Saltire Society, £8.95; *Shakespeare's Macbeth translated into Scots,* Robin Lorimer, Canongate, £12.95; *The Tragedie o Macbeth,* David Purves, Rob Roy Press, 44 St Patrick Sq. Edinburgh; *A Toosht o' Whigmaleeries,* and *Back O Bennachie,* both Sheena Blackhall, Hammerfield Publishing, 36 Hammerfield Avenue, Aberdeen, £3.00 and £3.95 We are constantly told that Scots language can't handle this and that, and that we should all switch to English. There are some who resist this fiercely, William Neill for one. Gavin Douglas's translations of Virgil's *Aeneid* were no doubt tackled with the intention of establishing the intrinsic scope and range of Scots; so, no doubting Neill's intention here. Point: if Scots can cope with Homer, who can't it handle?

The result is immediately captivating. Neill's almost savagely ordinary Scots proves equal to the task of conveying the heroic tones, yet never loses touch with the intimacies of human experience, the comic tragedy of everyday life.

George Bruce in his introduction quotes the Russian Burns translator Samuel Marshak on the importance of translation into native languages, enabling it to be loved by those people. The translated poem must be liberated anew, not from the text, but "free in spirit... planted again in new soil." Bruce also compares Chapman's owresetting with Neill's, finding in the latter "a release of energy" which isn't found in the former, and, especially at key moments like Odysseus's final return home, not only great emotional veracity, but he is also closer to the Greek original.

Here's a snatch from 'The Wanchancy Voyage', in which Odysseus and his crew encounter the sirens:

Than yin bi yin I stecht the lugs o ma feres
an than thay bund me haund an fuit in the ship
tae the steid o the most an round it wund the raip
syne sett thaim doun tae skelp the gray sea wi thair airs

Here we have, on the one hand, vivid writing, direct and easy to follow, and yet the poetic expression of the impact of the siren's song, even on the sea, has tremendous power. Barbara Robertson's illustrations have a curious antique modernity which complements Neill's masterly translation work, which well deserves to stand amongst the very best.

The next two items are in one sense contentious, since they are of the same text, Shakespeare's *Macbeth*. The first was David Purves's, and indeed a section of it appeared in *Chapman* some time ago. My initial response was to ask whether we wanted any translation in the first place, Scots being so uncomfortably close to English. Now, it is unquestionably true that Lorimer got the idea to do his translation from having read Purves's, and natu-

rally one wonders if Scots, or any language for that matter, is capable of more than one rendering of "Is this a dagger I see before me..." So, if justice there were, the comparisons (inevitable) would favour Purves. But justice is treacherous bitch. While both translations are in their ways noble efforts, there is beyond any doubt a dignity and a power in Lorimer's translation which Purves' more accessible work generally doesn't attain. What is lost in the latter is generally the rhythm and the poetry. Take the four lines at the end of Act I: in Purves

A'm settlit nou an set ti bend masell
doun ti this frichsum darg
Awa an begowk the warld wi yer fairest face
Yeir fauss face maun dern what yeir fauss hert kens

And in Lorimer:

Nou I'm determit, aa
ma strenth I'll bend tae du this fearsome deed.
Awa, begowk the time wi fairest shaws:
fauss face maun dern the saicret fauss hairt knaws.

Taking the sections as a whole, Lorimer's best preserves the lean poetic line, preserving the rhythm. Purves's is prosaic, especially in the first two lines, although his "begowk the warld" line is poetically better, Lorimer also manages a rhyming couplet, although neither quite achieves the tautness of Shakespeare in the last line. I could go on... The verdict: Lorimer's is the better, for poetic quality, originality of translation, for compression and nobility of expression, but Purves's perhaps has more general utility because less literary, poetic and easier to follow.

Lastly, two more booklets from Sheena Blackhall, *Back o Bennachie* and *A Toosht o' Whigmaleeries*, both produced from a very small publisher, no doubt an act of altruism. Blackhall is a prolific poet, and keeping up with her outpourings is a major problem. Good stuff there is in here in plenty, in Scots and English, bits of prose and translation mixed in, writing for children, but the setting is terrible, the poems are crammed into small print, with no attempt to order them into sections, which would much aid proper appreciation of them. It's long past time a more thoughtful, better arranged volume, indeed a *Selected Poems* was produced. With the best will in the world, reading these, and doing them full justice, is a struggle. *Joy Hendry*

Theatre Roundup

Whatever the burning issue of the day, theatre will muscle in and add to the debate. You need only look to the fuss that has surrounded David Mamet's *Oleanna* to see how big a stir can be produced by a play that exposes contemporary concerns (in this case the rise of the 'politically correct' and the redefinition of male–female relationships), but even without focusing so specifically on an issue, theatre routinely speaks for our times, in its slants, in its reinterpretations, in its newness. Where it doesn't, it ossifies and becomes irrelevant.

A recurring debate in Scotland, and therefore in Scottish theatre, is to do with nationalism and national identity. The stage has tended to deal with these subjects less in the specific content of plays than in the way these plays are performed. We're used to the idea now, but simply to transpose, say, Molière into a Scots register instead of the standard English that tradition dictates was not so very long ago something of a novelty. Since the success of writers such as Liz Lochhead and the inroads made particularly at the Royal Lyceum, it is unlikely that a Scottish company would now consider doing Molière in anything other than Scots, but it is important to recognise that to do so is a political act.

Many plays have addressed the issue of nationalism head on. Communicado's *Jock Tamson's Bairns* was one such elaborate and appropriately ambiguous attempt, and more recently David Greig with his company Suspect Culture has been looking to the nationalist upsurges in Eastern Europe, drawing comparisons with the Scottish mood. His double bill under the blanket heading of *Europe* was seen at the Arches Theatre, Glasgow, in July, and though the plays had a tendency to meander in directorial terms, politically Greig put his finger on the key dramatic conflict of our times. On the one hand we have an urge to celebrate patriotically the culture of which we are a part, yet on the other we are repulsed by the destruction that patriotism is capable of producing. We know what we mean when we talk of our sense of identity, but try and pin it down, define it, and it quickly turns elusive. These are the ambivalent areas that Greig is exploring and it will be interesting to get another look at his earlier play, *Stalinland*, which deals in similar themes, when it is produced at the Citizens' Theatre this autumn.

But so long as nationalism and identity are on the agenda, it seems relevant to ask what is uniquely and distinctively *Scottish* about the theatre that is produced here. The history of the Scottish stage is erratic and uneven. Though attempts have been made to restore the names of long-forgotten dramatists, it is impossible to claim the kind of continuity that has been enjoyed by the English stage from Shakespeare down. This does not preclude a distinctive style of theatre in Scotland today, but it does make it harder to identify it with certainty. We can talk confidently about a Scottish folk tradition, about story-telling, about poetry, even about music-hall and panto, but try and single out a uniquely Scottish drama (in the way you could a uniquely Polish one) and you'd be harder pressed.

Indeed for the most part, Scottish theatregoers see much the same plays as their English counterparts. Nevertheless I would argue that there *is* such a thing as a Scottish style. I wouldn't claim it to be unique or clear-cut, and it certainly doesn't apply to every production by every company. Its characteristics include a direct, open relationship with the audience, an ability and desire to assimilate other art forms and a fluid, integrated sense of the theatrical. We see it in the best work of Ian Brown at the Traverse and Gerry Mulgrew at Communicado; no doubt it has its roots in the music hall, the ceilidh and story-telling, and later the populist theatre of 7:84; but I would also suggest that the geographical fact of Scotland being a small country with the bulk of its population densely concentrated in an even smaller area (where, it should be noted, the world's largest annual arts festival takes place) means that the healthy artistic cross-fertilisation which is at the heart of this style, is an inevitable consequence. Musicians meet painters meet sculptors meet actors meet playwrights and, as soon as the climate is right for experiment, they meet again on the stage.

I don't need to force the facts too much to prove my point when looking at the Scottish contribution to this year's Mayfest. Everywhere from the classical to the left-of-centre, Scottish companies were teasing the senses, be it in the high-tech fun-fair theatrics of NVA's *Sabotage*, the DIY performance art of Clanjamfrie's *Somewhere...*, the symphonic shifts of TAG's *Sunset Song*, the music-theatre of the Scottish Chamber Orchestra's *VS*, or the mature blend of influences in the Tron/Dundee Rep co-production of *Macbeth*. There's too much diversity here to claim anything but the broadest links, but that diversity is in itself an indicator of Scottish theatre's eclecticism.

And if diversity is your thing, you couldn't have done better than *Sabotage* – so diverse that I would hesitate even to call it theatre. Taking over the Tramway's main space, the show consisted of a series of installations created by an international team of sculptors, scientists, performers, whizzkids and artists. The audience walks from installation to installation, supposedly on a journey both through the human body and from birth to death, all the while being bombarded by music, noise, light, projections and various disorientation effects. We watched through peep-holes as a couple copulated, listened to a discordant band of musical robots, stood in an elevator-like box that turned into a pulsating human heart and generally got shoved around for 90 minutes of sensory overload.

The limitation of *Sabotage* was that the many ideas behind the show were not clearly enough articulated in the performance itself. While I can appreciate director Angus Farquhar's desire for the production to have operated on a subconscious level, I also feel that a little less subtext – perhaps a running commentary through headphones –would have made the collage seem less open-ended. But if the overall result was unsatisfactory, *Sabotage* was still a fascinating 90 minutes and the generally unfavourable newspaper reviews failed fully to credit the tremendous level of ambition and considerable skill involved. It may not be the best, but *Sabotage* is certainly the most distinctive production that I have seen in a long time. How *Scottish* it is, is as ever debatable, but it is significant that Farquhar looks not to London but to Europe for inspiration and I can think of nowhere on this side of the Channel other than Glasgow where such a production might have been created.

A letter in *The Herald* praising Michael Boyd's *Macbeth*, enthused that it was worthy of the Royal Shakespeare Company. No, wrote journalist Jackie McGlone, making a rare appearance on the letters page, the RSC isn't nearly so good. And perhaps only in Scotland could you create such a sensitive production, rich in human warmth (no hard-edged RADA accents here), yet genuinely chilling. Having Iain Glen on board in the title role was a tremendous asset, but this was no imbalanced star-vehicle, rather an intellectually, physically and emotionally coherent interpretation that made sense at every turn. The production was alive with ideas, never showy or intrusive, but always sufficient to bring freshness to the text. Turning the witches into children was the most striking departure from tradition, bringing a sinister Gothic chill to the play's supernatural side. Elsewhere, whether it was Glen's opening seven-foot leap onto the stage or the banquet scenes that took place in some other room beyond our sight, the production repeatedly came up with new twists.

TAG's revival of its adaptation of Lewis Grassic Gibbon's *Sunset Song* made use of an even more subtle combination of forms. Since its first airing 18 months earlier, it had developed into an ever more subtle and delicate blend of theatrical elements – movement, music, lighting, performance and story-telling beating to the same organic pulse. The beguiling quality of director Tony Graham's production is that none of these component elements called undue attention to itself. The charm of *Sunset Song* was in the way it gradually drew us in, not with shock-tactics but with a cool and measured poise as gentle as the undulations of Sally Jacob's earthy set.

Both *Macbeth* and *Sunset Song* argue that there is a quality particular to Scottish theatre in the early 1990s. It goes beyond accent or sharing a Scottish experience, though I would hesitate before calling it a quality that was innately or exclusively Scottish. The important thing is that several companies here are currently producing mature, outward-looking, open-minded theatre. Distressingly, through lack of funding a director of Michael Boyd's calibre is producing only one straight play and one pantomime a year. At that rate of output, it'll be a while before there's sufficient a body of Scottish work to bother calling unique.

Mark Fisher

Pamphleteer

Taking on Pamphleteer is always a daunting business (and undoubtedly bad for the eyes) but it is also usually a rewarding one. Emil Rado, for example, born in Hungary in 1931 but a lecturer at Glasgow University since 1965. The poems gathered in *Painting Shadows on the Tilting Horizon* (Taranis Books, £3.99) deal with love and with death, with landscape and with nature. The work is unostentatious and in many ways stark. There is the quality, though rarely the comparable craft, of MacCaig in some of these poems but like MacCaig they usually manage to touch or reach you in an unexpected way. This is from 'A Coppiced Friendship':

...the sap still runs in the stump,
and buds are ready to burst on its new-born
branches.

I tend it with watchful attention – and secateurs.

Direct work which is sometimes unchallenging, though here that makes a welcome change, a book well worth investigating.

Rebel Inc are new to what I'm sure they would disdain as "the Scottish literary scene" but they clearly haven't been mucking about, quickly establishing a distinctive profile for themselves. Three titles here then from their publications squad (and check out the magazine if you haven't already). Firstly, I've always been taken with Graham Fulton's work, his placing and precision of things, a hard language with sharp teeth he's quite happy to use. This is from 'The Milk' the opening poem from *This*:

Upstairs
the baby is
good as gold. His eyes
are closed, fingers small, pillow
is wet because of the blood that leaks
from the yawning crack in his head.
The cot-bars the sitter slammed it against
because it kept asking to be fed
are stained but un-
broken.

My main reservation about Fulton's work is his occasional wilful disintegration of his own text which often does more harm than good. Usually his writing is strong enough to survive the most vicious contortions. I was less impressed with *Three Edinburgh Writers* where the work can be a wee bit too self-con-

sciously tough for its own good. Still, there is some good hard-edged poetry here from Barry Graham ('Hawkeye Haughey'), Kevin Williamson ('Don't Talk To Me About Scotland') and Paul Reekie ('Victim of a Miracle'). Much of this work is performance-oriented, which is fine, but a dominance of repetitive rhyme and rhythm can get pretty flat on the written page. Of these three publications though, *Baz Poems* from Kevin Cadwallender, stands out. This sequence of poems takes us through the grimy, dangerous, destructive life and times of Baz: "Like part of his childhood/ got fucked up by the bastard brood/ of Bruce Lee and Eva Braun". This is a dark, funny, sad, painful book, even the young Baz is mad, bad and dangerous to know:

Baz at a loss
for answers gassed
the school hamster
with a blown out
bunsen burner.

"What kind of moron are you?"
asked Mr. Chapman.

It was the first time
I ever saw a teacher bleed.

Get this one if you can. All of these Rebel Inc publications are limited editions of one hundred, all priced at £1.99 and available from Rebel Inc, PO Box 491, Edinburgh, EH12 9DY.

An American poet who rarely receives the recognition he deserves in this country is James Deahl. The thirty poems gathered in *Opening The Stone Heart* (cover price £3.50, available from Envoi Poets Publications, Pen Ffordd, Newport, Dyfed, SA42 0QT) were all written in the course of a British reading tour, from tip to tail, and the work as a whole adds up to an on-the-road travelogue. Moving from 'Pentecost at Mallaig' to 'Neap Tide in South Wales' and much more in between. Deahl's writing is clean, sparse and vivid. He is a sensitive observer/commentator and here he catches snapshots of land and history, sea and shore, the life moving around him. This is an extract from 'Neap Tide':

And so the children shriek
their cartwheel days. In the briny grass
of salt pastures

they chase long-legged waders
through a shadow of headlands
tossed by eel-surge waves.

Appropriately, more than a hint of Dylan Thomas lurking in between the lines here, a good way of tuning in to wherever you happen to be: taste the language, listen to the sound, but most of all, keep your eyes open. Deahl's always are.

David Craig's *The Grasshopper's Burden* (Littlewood Arc, £5.95) can sometimes seem a little strained, almost too densely textured for comfort: "Eyes like black anemones, tender convexities/ Glossy with mucus, scan the shoreline for us", (from 'Neighbours'). Nonetheless, as lines like these also illustrate, the poetry is complex, restless and sometimes jolting. Craig is constantly pushing at the language itself, forging a technique and style uniquely his own: new images in new places make this a collection well worth taking some time over. From the same publisher comes *Graffiti for Hard Hearts* (£5.95) by Donald Atkinson. These poems show considerable stylistic diversity, from the almost skeletal to the crushed and crunched. There is a sentimental underbelly to some of this work that leaves it a bit too bare and vulnerable, defusing its genuine power. That is to be found in poems such as the 'Whale Bone Man', lodged in the whale's throat:

> Everything he eats
> enters lengthy negotiations
> to get by me.
> Before my arrival
> he would swallow anything
>
> like the young man
> taken in and half digested
> before my time

Of Eros and of Dust, edited by Steve Anthony (The Oscar Press, £5.99) features the work of poets who are "…gay, straight, or somewhere in between". This selection can be unsettling, focusing on the city, on sexuality, the instabilities of the world in the midst of which most of us have to function. There is a lot of good work on offer here from the likes of Edwin Morgan, Christopher Whyte, Tamar Yoseloff, Jackie Kay and U.A. Fanthorpe to name but a handful. These poems can be dark, vicious and sensitive by turns, not a comfortable book by any means, but one which confronts and elucidates the way we live our lives and looks at where we may be going.

On a smaller scale but equally worthwhile is *Parcel of Rogues* (£1.00, Clocktower Press, 24 Dundas Street, Stromness, Orkney, KW16 3BZ): "work in progress" from the likes of Janice Galloway, James Kelman and Gordon Legge. I particularly enjoyed Irvine Welsh's "Trainspotting At Leith Central Station", sadly now gutted and gone, but if you are at all interested in the directions of modern Scottish fiction this short collection offers valuable inroads. Also worth taking a look at is *Past Dancing* (from Jim Glen, 47 West Holmes Gardens, Musselburgh, EH21 8QW, £1.50 inc. p&p). This is the first collection of work gathered by the Central Writers Workshop and with work from Glen himself alongside Ian McDonough, Susan Chaney and many more, suggests that the group is a strong one and adds up to a varied and accomplished amalgam of prose and poetry well worth having.

Finally, two recent collections of poetry deserve some attention. Chris Bendon's *Perspective Lessons, Virtual Lines* (Rockingham Press, £5.95) is distinctive in its fusion of coherence and restless experimentation, the two don't always sit comfortably together. Aside from the diversity of technique and perspective on offer here though there is a rigorousness in the language which ensures Bendon's work rarely fails to make impact:

> Small bodies scuttle, crablike
> Against the green lashing filth of water:
> An air come free of masts, the one time
> Forest gone, forever departing in
> museum photographs…

The poems from John Gohorry in his second collection, *Talk Into The Late Evening* (Peterloo Poets £6.95) display a similar ruggedness in approach to language and a comparable concern with structure, never settling for the mundane or predictable. Both of these writers are consistently pushing their work to find new ways of doing things. Gohorry at his best forges an odd blend of the elegant and the harsh that singles out his work: "…a few birds drowned and dismembered/ among the reedblades, their throats already whispering/ for the service of maggots", (from 'New Year's Day at Grafham Water'). This is a finely honed and polished collection on which to conclude discussion of a series of books, all of which will reward your time and attention.

Thom Nairn

Catalogue

I heard the carping voices wi ma ain lugs, in the early days of the Canongate Classics: nowadays, happily, the debate is, mostly, more to do with what ought to be next in the series rather than whether there should be a series at all and Canongate publishing instead us living authors. Quite apart from making available texts which would otherwise be out of print, the standard of text preparation and critical prolegomenae has become very high, outshining those of Penguin Classics I've encountered recently, though perhaps because the contents are more interesting to start with. The latest arrivals bring the catalogue to fifty, No. 50 itself being *An Autobiography* (£5.99), introduced by Peter Butter, the leading authority on Edwin Muir. Meanwhile, *Listen to the Voice* (£5.99) is a selection of Iain Crichton Smith stories which finds Douglas Gifford talking in the introduction, *in re* Murdo, about Brecht's *Verfremmsdung* effect, which seems pretty sapient to me. Back the way, No. 48 is J MacDougall Hay's *Gillespie* (£6.99).

Iain Crichton Smith has been having a good time of it over the last year or so, what with his *Thoughts of Murdo* from Balnain, *An Honourable Death* (Macmillan, £13.99), a kind of dramatised biography of Major-General Sir Hector MacDonald, and of course the *Collected Poems* from Carcanet (£25), one of the most valuable *Collecteds* for years. With ICS's poetry on the Higher menu, a *Collected* in the one hand, perhaps, and Carol Gow's *Mirror and Marble* (Lines Review Editions, £9.95) in the other ought to guarantee a pass, the latter being a critical study specifically of the poetry (warning: thigh-deep in footnotes).

There are some magnificent photographs in *Granite & Green* from Mainstream (£14.99), Angus & Patricia Macdonald's sequel to their successful *Above Edinburgh and South-East Scotland*, a blend of aerial pix, narrative and well-chosen literary selections. *Edinburgh: A Celebration*, by contrast, is merely an extravagant exercise in civic pride, the sort of thing you are given if a visiting mayor or some such moderately important person to whom it doesn't matter that the chosen typeface is virtually unreadable. The man who brought us *The Edinburgh Graveyard Guide*, Michael Turnbull, now presents *Edinburgh Characters* (St Andrew Press, £5.50). Far from being a dusty name-check, it makes for a lively and fascinating browse. Alternatively, you can turn to the *Scottish Biographical Dictionary* from Chambers (£25), wherein footballer Maurice Johnston rubs shoulders with Physician, poet and humanist Arthur Johnston (1587–1641). Another fascinating browse and a valuable, if time-stamped, resource.

From biography to hagiography and an attractive series of lives of Celtic saints from Floris Books, based on original sources, encompassing Saints Columba, Bride, Patrick and Brendan (£2.50 each). Without the mock-King James prose style "Thou healedst folk of thine own kin yesterday, and thou hast not waited to heal us today", I wonder how the saints would seem – more or less real? I prefer the folk tales in Floris's reprint of Padraig Colum's *The King of Ireland's Son* (£5.99). Don't know what that says about me, since it's supposed to be for 8–11-year-olds. The Saltire Society, meanwhile, reprints Ian Grimble's *Strathnaver Trilogy*, beginning with *Chief of Mackay* (£9.95), a thorough, passionate and above all readable history of the far northwest of Scotland. Also John Sibbald Gibson's *Deacon Brodie: Father to Jekyll & Hyde* (£8.95), drawing so extensively on contemporary material that it is hard to know what is true and what is purpure invention.

Home Secretary Michael Howard is apparently proposing to toughen up prison regimes. Reading John Steele's *The Bird That Never Flew* (Sinclair Stevenson, £15.95), the only avenue available seems to be to legalise death in custody. Steele's story is hard, hard, the system follows a mindless routine of its own that no one, least of all those with the power to, seems willing to change. As a social document it has the ring of authenticity, and no little detail; as a human story, that matters less than the struggle to express the individual spirit. James Kelman's *The Burn* (Minerva, £4.99) covers similar urban terrain in fictive terms with the candour and humanity we've come to expect. Charles Palliser's *The Sensationist* (Picador, £4.99) seems pretty flimsy by comparison: though the writing is of a very high standard, the narrative's sincerity always seems disingenuous beyond intention. One more biography in passing, Andro Linklater's *Compton Mackenzie: A Life* (Hogarth Press, £9.99) retails the author of *Whisky Galore*, one who lived life as a music-hall turn.

David Milsted's *Telling Stories* (Harper Collins, £15.99) is too long. The padding is of Savile Row quality, but it *is* padding. Hard to summarise the content, except to describe it as dealing with the fractal dimension of 'truth'. Nicolas Bouvier's *The Way of the World* (Polygon, £8.95) is a sort of *sur la rue* cum *Journey to the East* trip from Bosnia to Afghanistan made in the early 1950s – a route almost completely riven by warfare subsequently, one can't help noticing. Recording an inward journey, Bashir Maan's *The New Scots* (John Donald, £9.50) is a lucid and valuable account of the Asian community in Scotland. From the Nordic Language Secretariat comes *Minority Languages: the Scandinavian Experience*, proceedings of a conference held at the Scandic Crown, Edinburgh, in 1990 and a useful overview on the subject.

Something about William Scammell's poem about John McEnroe in *The Game* (Peterloo Poets, £6) somehow captures what it is to be English: as though seeing only his uncourtly behaviour and not his supreme genius, its beauty bound up in its ferocity, stands as a metaphor for English myopia. I may say that using 'Abo' as an internal rhyme with 'Little Mo' in a poem about Evonne Goolagong doesn't undermine my case. Myopics beware the latest works of Peter Russell to appear from the University of Salzburg Press: a magnifying glass reveals uneven value – though value there is – in these four volumes, from animadversion and verse in Italian and English (*Poetic Asides I & II*), to an impressionistic summary of his long-term friendship with Ezra Pound (*The Pound Connection*): his defence of Pound's politics is unconvincing, his remarks on McLuhan's interest in effect at the expense of cause genuinely sharp. A good editor would help, and, having been marginalised by 'The Movement', Russell's poetry deserves reassessment in these less xenophobic times. *The Image of Woman as a Figure of the Spirit*, a theoretical work, curiously has a picture of three males gazing from the cover. Also in the Salzburg boat are William Oxley's *The Playboy* (£5.95, available through Acu-

men) and *The Whiteness of Her Becoming* by Fred Beake (£6.50). Beake's collection is a stimulating read, allowing for a compulsively alienating layout much of the time; Oxley's long poem too is writing of a high standard, but the younger and more female a reader you are, I suspect, the less you will enjoy it.

The male gaze has become as much a bone of contention in poetry as painting since Walcott was taken to task for his cypher-women. Solipsism is some kind of defence, I suppose, as well as a convenient link to Sebastian Barker's *The Dream of Intelligence* (Littlewood Arc, £9.95) – a hugely ambitious epic poem dealing with the life and thought of Nietzsche. Barker's selected poems *Guarding the Border* is lately come from Entharmion (£7.95) too. Perhaps it's their coming from Carcanet that makes Barker's rough contemporaries Eavan Boland and John Ash seem younger: Boland's *Outside History* (£6.95) shimmers and glistens with moist Irish cadences. Ash's *The Burnt Pages* (£6.95) matches its title with a brittle brilliance of imagery, though one hopes his references to Koechlin and Merikanto (composers) are made in a spirit of celebration rather than obfuscation.

How unfortunate to be tagged 'Poet of the '80s'. Peter Reading's *3 in 1* (Chatto, £7.99) brilliantly substantiates the claim, being *Ukulele Music, Diplopic* and, especially, *C*, in one volume. Trouble is, so too does *Evagatory* (Chatto, £5.99), published in the '90s, and frankly a bit tired by comparison. Mark Ford's *Landlocked* (Chatto, £5.99) sums itself up in the first poem, 'Passion Play', linguistic and poetic skill, humour, unexpected insights, the language of soccer *Verfremmsdung*ed. Finally (they think it's all over...) two anthologies well worth nebbing: *The Forward Book of Poetry 1993* (Forward Publishing, £5.95), culled from some of last year's literary magazines, books, competitions etc: a useful snapshot, if inevitably not a full team photograph, of current UK poetry. *Grandchildren of Albion* (New Departures, £9.99) follows the 1969 *Children of Albion: Poetry of the Underground* in being a generous umbrella for poetry in its broadest sense in the modern multi-cultural British Isles. Sometimes so busily presented that it's hard to identify authors, the energy is not wasted nevertheless.

Notes on Contributors

Thomas Allen: Born Blantyre 1957 of underclass background and chequered criminal history. Was encouraged to write by a judge and in the past year has had various stories, poetry and articles published.

Sheena Blackhall: Born Aberdeen 1947. Poet, short-story writer, illustrator. She has published eight volumes of poetry, two collections of stories.

Valentina Bold: Daughter of Alan Bold.

Robert Calder: Having been submerged in 19th century Scottish philosophy for years, a waterspout now appears in the form of *A School of Thinking: Realism & Revival of Learning* (Polygon), discussing Macmurray's thought, his Scottish contemporaries and antecedents.

Sandie Craigie: Edinburgh writer, born in the Old Town. Part of the *Rebel Inc* team.

A R C Duncan was Macmurray's assistant at both London and Edinburgh. Thirty years head of the Philosophy dept, Queens University, Kingston, Ontario, he remained close to Macmurray, of whom his *On the Nature of Persons* is the first book-length account.

Bill Duncan teaches English at Carnoustie High School. With his colleagues he has collated a study-pack on Iain Crichton Smith: details c/o *Chapman*.

Mark Fisher is Managing Editor of *Theatre Scotland* and senior theatre correspondent for *The List*.

Stanley M Harrison: Associate Professor of Philosophy at Marquette University, Milwaukee, a prime mover in the Macmurray Centenary Conference.

Brian Holton: b Galashiels 1949, teaches Chinese at Durham University. He is translating the young 'Misty School' poet Yang Lian, while continuing *Men o the Mossflow,* his Scots version of *The Water Margin.*

Harvey Holton: b Galashiels the same day in 1949, now settled in Fife. Recently Writing Fellow at Duncan of Jordanston College, publications include *Finn, Four Fife Poets.*

Michael Hulse is director of the European Festival of Literature being held in Köln next year, poet (recently *Eating Strawberries in the Necropolis*, Harvill) and co-editor of Bloodaxe's recently-controversial *The New Poetry.*

Robert Alan Jamieson: Shetland-born poet and novelist recently appointed to the Soutar Fellowship at Perth.

Fred Johnston: poet & critic b Belfast, based in Galway. Extensively published. Initiated Cuirt, Galway's Poetry Festival, in 1986.

Linda McCann has been Writing Fellow for the Universities of Glasgow & Strathclyde. She has a forthcoming collection of short stories from Polygon and is currently working on her first novel and a book of poems.

Ruth McIlroy: born Wales, now living in Edinburgh, recently working as a Shiatsu instructor.

Christine McNeill: b Vienna, lived in England since 1970, teaching German in adult education in Norfolk. First collection, *Kissing the Night* just published by Bloodaxe.

Catriona Malan: Schoolteacher living in Helensburgh. Stories and poetry in various anthologies, including the HarperCollins.

Thom Nairn: Managing Editor of *Cencrastus,* a widely-published critic and poet.

Ma Zhiyuan: arguably the greatest dramatist of the Mongol dynasty and an admired lyric poet.

Colin Nicholson teaches English & Scottish literature at Edinburgh University. Editor of a number of critical studies, most recently Polygon's *Poem Purpose & Place.*

Qiao Jifu: a native of Taiyuan, famous in his (early 14th century) day as playwright and witty, colloquial poet.

Mario Relich is an Open University Course Tutor and occasional reviewer for *The Scotsman.*

Iain Crichton Smith: One of the century's great Gaelic writers, as gifted in English – formerly a teacher of English at Oban.

Christopher Whyte: poet and critic currently teaching Scottish Literature at Glasgow University.